David & Charles Locomotive Studies

THE STANIER 4-6-0s
OF THE LMS
(The Jubilees, Class 5s
and the BR Standard Class 5s)

J. W. P. Rowledge, CEng, MIMechE
and
Brian Reed

DAVID & CHARLES
NEWTON ABBOT LONDON
NORTH POMFRET (VT) VANCOUVER

ISBN 0 7153 7385 4

Library of Congress Catalog Card Number: 77-74358

© DAVID & CHARLES (PUBLISHERS) LTD 1977

Set in 10 on 11 English
and printed in Great Britain
by Biddles of Guildford
for David & Charles (Publishers) Limited
Brunel House Newton Abbot Devon

Published in the United States of America
by David & Charles Inc
North Pomfret Vermont 05053 USA

Published in Canada
by Douglas David & Charles Limited
1875 Welch Street North Vancouver BC

David & Charles Locomotive Studies

Published Titles

The Steam Locomotives of Eastern Europe, by A. E. Durrant
Steam Locomotives in Industry, by The Industrial Locomotive Society
Steam Locomotives of the South African Railways, Vols 1 and 2, by D. F. Holland
Steam Locomotives of the East African Railways, by R. Ramaer
The British Internal-Combustion Locomotive: 1894-1940, by Brian Webb
Diesel-hydraulic Locomotives of the Western Region, by Brian Reed
English Electric Main Line Diesels of BR, by Brian Webb
The Drummond Greyhounds of the LSWR, by D. L. Bradley

Locomotive Monographs

General Editor:
O. S. Nock, BSc, CEng, FICE, FIMechE
The GWR Stars, Castles & Kings, Parts 1 and 2, by O. S. Nock
The LNWR Precursor Family, by O. S. Nock
The Stirling Singles of the Great Northern Railway, by K. H. Leech and M. Boddy
Gresley Pacifics, Parts 1 and 2, by O. S. Nock
The Southern King Arthur Family, by O. S. Nock
The GWR Standard Gauge 4-4-0s, Vols 1 and 2, by O. S. Nock
The LMS Royal Scots, by O. S. Nock

CONTENTS

Jubilee ascending the south bank of Shap with a Manchester-Glasgow train, and showing the well-known but now defunct Scout Green signalbox and the tall up-line stop signal. *(W. J. V. Anderson)*

Jacket: front: Preserved AW-built Black Five No. 5428 now named *Eric Treacy* alongside the preserved three-cylinder NBL-built Jubilee No. 5593 *Kolhapur.* Both engines equipped with BR aws apparatus. *(Ivo Peters)*; *back:* The last-built of the thirty Caprotti 5MTs built 1956-57. BR standard whistle horizontal on firebox top; model 1C tender. *(British Railways)*

CHAPTER ONE

INTRODUCTION

When W. A. Stanier came from Swindon to assume office as chief mechanical engineer of the London, Midland & Scottish Railway (LMSR) on 1 January 1932, the need of that railway for a large stud of competent express passenger engines had been ameliorated only on the Western Division trunk line by the 70 Royal Scots of 1927 and 1930. Over the main lines of the rest of the system outworn and outdated six-coupled two-cylinder and four-cylinder simples and four-coupled simples and compounds maintained the working inefficiently, as shown through the statistics initiated by Sir Josiah Stamp after becoming president in 1925, and pursued by him and by J. H. Follows and E. J. H. Lemon.

Faith had been strong at Crewe that performance of the Claughton four-cylinder 4-6-0s could be improved, and in 1928 a score of these engines had been provided with new enlarged Belpaire boilers of Derby design, coded as G9½S; and ten of these rebuilds had also been given Caprotti valve gear. Though the performance was improved, all the design faults remained that had led to poor availability, unreliability, and expensive maintenance.

To supplement the Royal Scots in the next lower power category a new beginning therefore had been made under Fowler in 1930 by rebuilding with new Royal Scot-type frames and three cylinders two of the large-boiler Claughtons, 5971 and 5902 (later 5500 and 5501), and then putting in hand for the 1932 programme what were really 40 further new locomotives (later 5502-41) to this 5XP power classification design. These three-cylinder parallel-boiler locomotives became known colloquially as the Baby Scots; officially, but only from 1937, they were known as the Patriot class, and they actually did replace 40 Claughtons bearing the same (pre-1934) numbers that were withdrawn in 1932-33.

Replacement of many of the Claughtons, none at that time more than 20 years old, was justified by a Locomotive Committee minute that the class 'give much trouble with trailing axleboxes, and the new type will give a 12 per cent increase in power with 24 per cent less maintenance';

these were by no means the only difficulties.

Also included in the 1932 locomotive construction programme were ten 'superheated converted' Prince of Wales 4-6-0s and five new-design 2-8-0s; but when the year's programme was reviewed by Stanier on his accession the credits allocated for these were diverted to fifteen more three-cylinder 5XP locomotives, ten of which were to be of the Patriot design, becoming 5542-51, and the other five of which saw the light as the first Crewe-built taper-boiler Stanier 5XP 4-6-0s which, from April 1935, were known as the Jubilee class. The first design-diagram for the latter was dated June 1932.

None of the first forty new Patriots was delivered until after Stanier had taken charge, and by the time the last of the fifty was introduced in 1934 they had an obsolete look, though not an obsolete standard of performance. Stanier made no attempt to countermand this work, though he had really come to the LMSR to inaugurate a whole new locomotive era. With motive power urgently needed, he was satisfied to confirm the design sponsored by his two predecessors for the G9½S boiler allied to the Royal Scot drive and chassis, and to have his taper boiler put on what was essentially the same chassis only for the last five of the locomotives for which finance had already been granted. The line of descent was made clear by the use of the term 'Improved Claughtons' in the first few Locomotive Committee minutes referring to the Jubilees; also, at least one published reference dubbed them 'Improved Baby Scots'.

Despite a conception for future LMSR motive power based on relatively few standard classes, Stanier concurrently initiated a scheme to fit Swindon-type taper boilers to almost every substantial existing class. The standard boiler chart issued in April 1933 showed the new 3A taper boiler as suited to 129 Claughtons and to seventy ex-LYR four-cylinder 4-6-0s and ten four-cylinder 4-6-4Ts, though actually it was applied only to the new Jubilees. Similarly the 3B taper boiler was shown as applicable to 246 Prince of Wales 4-6-0 rebuilds and to two proposed 2-8-0s, but was actually used only on the Stanier Class 5. This proposed programme

involving many new boilers and comparatively few new locomotives gave way over the next seven years to the construction of over a thousand new locomotives to a conception never envisaged before 1932 on the LMSR.

When Stanier arrived at Euston a few Pacifics were justified to supplant the Royal Scots on long through Anglo-Scottish runs with heavy trains to the accelerated schedules proposed for the summer of 1932, and the two first 4-6-2s were the earliest of his passenger types, though they did not begin work until 1933. Just as urgent was a development from the then new parallel-boiler 5XP into a future standard 4-6-0 with a maximum axle load not above twenty tons in conjunction with low hammer-blow and linear loadings not exceeding 3.5 ton/ft of coupled wheelbase and 2.5 ton/ft of engine-and-tender wheelbase. This was to cope with the increasing loads and speeds on the main lines of the Western, Central, Midland and Northern Divisions and, as the proposed large reboilering programme came to be given up, to permit the retirement of hundreds of Claughton, Prince of Wales, LYR and Caledonian 4-6-0s.

Though the major requirement in 1932 was for express passenger power, Stanier probably had in mind from the beginning a two-cylinder general-purpose 4-6-0, for he came to the LMSR fresh from experiences with the first batch of Halls on the GWR. Indeed, E. S. Cox has stated (*Locomotive Panorama*) that the mixed-traffic 4-6-0 diagram drawn up at Euston 'owed a great deal to the GWR Halls'. Nevertheless a three-cylinder version with 15½in cylinders was considered in 1932 before the detailed design of the celebrated two-cylinder Class 5 was begun from a Euston design-diagram dated July 1932. That engine owed nothing to 'LMSR descent', for in the mixed-traffic category there was no intermediate stage corresponding to the early Patriots, and neither the Horwich Crab 2-6-0s nor Crewe's modified Prince of Wales design (with Caprotti motion) mentioned earlier could be taken as a basis.

Nevertheless, in actuality if not in conception, Class 5 was a development of the forty Crewe-built Moguls (Nos. 2945-84) that formed Stanier's first main-line construction for the LMSR. Thus was repeated the older GWR succession that 'production' mixed-traffic 4-6-0s followed mixed-traffic 2-6-0s only after a

Above: Official photograph of the first Class 5 of all, Vulcan Foundry's works number 4565. Note thin red line around cab windows, peculiar to Nos. 5020-69. Tall chimney reaching to height of 12ft 10in.

Left: First Jubilee, the original No. 5552 newly built, with new-built Fowler old-standard 3500-gallon tender attached. Photograph taken during the few weeks in the summer of 1934 while the engine was attached to Preston depot, hence the smokebox shed plate 27. *(J. B. Radford collection)*

measurable span of time, though here a time much shorter than the 18 years on the GWR. In this case, unusually, the 4-6-0 had the same firebox, grate, number and diameter of tubes, and back-end boiler barrel diameter as the Mogul.

As with the three-cylinder express Jubilees, the first Class 5 construction in 1934 began with credits already sanctioned for something else, in this case ten improved Caprotti Prince of Wales 4-6-0s with 6ft 3in wheels and ten light 4-6-0s to a new design for the Scottish section. The amounts approved, totalling £130,000, were transferred to the construction of the first twenty Crewe-built Class 5 engines, and the sanctioned engines were never built.

In projecting the new standard classes, Stanier did not insist on strict standardisation of major components. Originally a single standard boiler was proposed for the mixed-traffic 4-6-0 and the freight 2-8-0, but this idea was not carried into effect, and comparatively minor differences in structure, length and tubes were always found, and prevented interchangeability. Thus Stanier differed from his mentor, Churchward, who insisted on strict standardisa-

tion but could not get full interchangeability because Swindon shop equipment and methods could not effect it in his time. Stanier did not enforce absolute standardisation, though had he done so the shop equipment and methods at Crewe and Derby could have given full interchangeability.

To suit the lengthy daily diagrammed mileage per engine that was a major point in the Stamp-Follows-Lemon operating policy, such a locomotive scheme had to be adapted to handling by pooled crews and to working under common user, with inter-divisional handling in the course of a day. This desideratum applied in the design stage to all Stanier main-line locomotives, and was achieved most notably by the Black Fives and Class 8F 2-8-0s; successful common-user handling by crews and maintenance staffs of all divisions was a feature also of the four-cylinder Pacifics, three-cylinder Jubilee 4-6-0s and two-cylinder 2-6-4Ts.

In appointing Stanier as chief mechanical engineer the LMSR directors were well aware that he was likely to sweep away existing locomotive practice and traditions. One of his principal remits may well have been to do just that, for through the first nine years of the company's existence no kind of satisfaction had been given by the locomotive department, and none was in sight. Yet the board could hardly have visualised the upset and expense over some five years of the new regime arising from Stanier's initial insistence on Swindon ideas of low-temperature superheat being applied to the early engines of five classes. The great labour and material costs involved in the numerous changes in superheaters, flues, tubes, and copper and steel tubeplates wiped out for several years the savings that could have been brought by the superior day-after-day performance of over 250 otherwise most effective locomotives.

CHAPTER TWO

THE JUBILEES

When the first taper-boiler Class 5XP orders were placed in 1933 only a handful of Stanier engines—Moguls and the first two Pacifics—was on the rails. The pressing need for effective main-line power, the available base of the Patriot design, and Stanier's confidence in his own conceptions with many practices new to the LMSR, led to no fewer than 113 of the new type being ordered within three or four months. Of these, five (Nos. 5552-56) to the first order, then forty-eight (Nos. 5607-54) to a subsequent order, were to come from Crewe, and ten (Nos. 5655-64) in a separate order from Derby. All these railway-built locomotives were delivered 1934-35 (see Tables I and V). The first, No. 5552 from Crewe, was exhibited at Euston on 23 April 1934.

Then in November 1933 an order for fifty was placed with the North British Locomotive Co. Ltd. (NBL), delivery being asked for the next summer. In an effort to achieve this, NBL in April 1934 decided to divide the order between Hyde Park and Queen's Park works. This did not have the desired effect, for the twenty-five from Hyde Park were delivered between 28 June and 29 September 1934; Queen's Park did not deliver its first engine until 3 November 1934, and the last engine was not sent off until 6 February 1935. Hyde Park engines bore NBL works numbers 24115-39, and LMSR numbers 5557-81, and were delivered to the LMSR at St. Rollox. The Queen's Park twenty-five had NBL works numbers 24140-64 and LMSR numbers 5582-5606, being delivered to Polmadie depot, adjacent to the works.

Quoted price for the fifty engines and tenders was £286,000, or £5,720 each, but another £7,000 was added on the contract for extras. Cost of raw materials, including bought-in finished items such as injectors, safety-valves and lubricators, amounted to £123,819 for the engines and £28,526 for the tenders, plus £618 for sundry blocks, tests, and the like. The sum of £140,037 remaining from the contract price was insufficient for wages and overheads, and NBL suffered a big loss.

In view of present-day (1976) prices some of the costs in 1934 are interesting. A 6ft 3in cast-steel driving wheel centre was priced at £23.30 rough, and its 6ft 9in tyre at £16.60; frame plates cost £9.60 per ton, and an outside connecting rod forging of manganese-molybdenum steel cost £12.80. All fifty cast-iron chimneys for the contract were obtained for less than £200, and fifty sets of superheater elements (fourteen bifurcated elements per set) were priced at £3,009. One hundred outside cylinder castings were charged at only £571 rough, and the fifty inside-cylinder castings (including a saddle extension) grossed £430, these last two amounts being NBL charged foundry costs without overheads.

In 1935-36 a further seventy-eight locomotives (Nos. 5665-5742) were built at Crewe under two

Above: Broadside of one of the 27ft 7in wheelbase engines as built in 1936, with domed barrel and sloping-throatplate firebox. Steam sanding; no hot-water de-sanders. Six washout plugs and two handholes on firebox side. *(British Railways)*

Left: NBL Hyde Park-built locomotive of 27ft 7in wheelbase; Stanier 4000-gallon 15ft 0in wheelbase tender attached. *(Mitchell Library)*

lot numbers (see Table I), and the total of 191 formed the most numerous class of six-coupled passenger engines built during the twenty-five years of the LMSR, and in fact was the most numerous six-coupled passenger class built for any Group railway through the era 1923-47. Of the seventy-eight engines of 1935-36, thirty had been projected for outside manufacturers as part of the 1935 programme, but this work was transferred to Crewe and the sanctioned 'outside credits' diverted to fifty Class 5 mixed-traffic 4-6-0s ordered from Vulcan Foundry.

As part of Stanier's standardisation programme the taper-boiler Class 5XP engines had a few parts (axleboxes, bogies and the like) in common with other classes; and boiler-back fittings, injectors and so on were to LMSR standards that Stanier did not alter. The many new details of boiler, running gear, suspension and motion followed the principles of concurrent Stanier classes as listed in the description of the Class 5 mixed-traffic engines in the fourth chapter of this book.

To meet the loading gauges of the various divisions, maximum width was restricted to 8ft 7in over the running plate and 8ft 6in over cab sides. The 3500-gallon Fowler-type tenders attached to some locomotives were narrower than the cab (7ft 1in tank width), but the 3500-gallon 'new type' and 4000-gallon Stanier type were full width (8ft 6in). With a boiler pitch of 8ft 11in the overall height of locomotives Nos. 5552-5664 was 13ft 2¾in, but to give wider route availability the later engines, Nos. 5665-5742, were provided with shorter chimneys extending to 12ft 11⅝in with the same boiler pitch. Similarly the cab roof height of 13ft 2¾in in the railway-built Nos. 5552-56 and 5607-64 was reduced to 12ft 10⅝in in the NBL batch and to 12ft 11⅞in in Nos. 5665-5742, but the footplate height above rails was the same in all instances. Subsequently some engines got an intermediate size of chimney that brought overall height up to 13ft 1⅛in, but this and other variations, which included in later days some BR chimneys, were not always immediately apparent.

The first fifty-three Crewe-built engines followed the Patriot wheelbase divisions exactly, and had the same central-pivot bogies of only 6ft 3in wheelbase. At that time the Stanier standard bogie had not been evolved, though a 6ft 6in base unit had been applied early in 1933 to the Royal Scot that toured North America. The first two Pacifics, because of their size and weight, had the special bogie base of 7ft 6in, and

TABLE I DETAILS OF ORDERS FOR LMSR 5XP JUBILEE CLASS 4-6-0

Date of authorisation	Year of introduction	No of locos	LMSR Lot No	Builder	Works order	Works Nos	Sanctioned cost /loco & tender	LMSR running Nos
5/1933	1934	5	97	Crewe	381	163-7	£5,700	5552-6
6/1933	1934-5	48	112	Crewe	388	168-215	£6,600	5607-54
6/1933	1934-5	10	113	Derby	0-8610	—	£6,600	5655-64
c.10/1933	1934-5	50	118	NBL	L885	24115-64(1)	£5,720	5557-5606
6/1934	1935-6	30	121	Crewe	396	263-92	£6,400	5665-94
7/1935	1936	48	129	Crewe	398	293-340(2)	£5,813	5695-5742

(1) NBL Works Nos 24115-39 Hyde Park; 24140-64 Queen's Park.
(2) Last locomotive marked with a Crewe number appears to have been No 5723; all Crewe numbers are "Second Series".

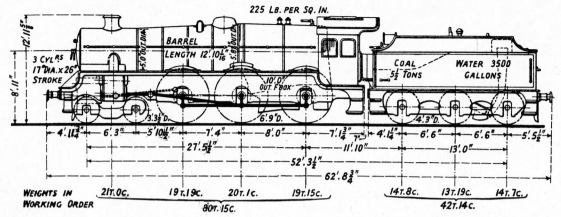

the bogie was of the side-bearer type used from then onwards. Coincident with the three-cylinder taper-boiler 5XP design that for the three-cylinder 2-6-4T was under way, and by the time NBL was ordering material for its fifty engines a bogie standard between the 4-6-0s (leading) and 2-6-4Ts (trailing) had been devised with double coil spring lateral control and side bearers; it had a wheelbase of 6ft 6in, and the NBL main frames were altered slightly to take this. The ten Derby-built engines, Nos. 5655-64, and the seventy-eight Crewe-built locomotives Nos. 5665-5742 of 1935-36, also had this new standard. The bogie pivot line was retained, so that the locomotive wheelbase became 1½in longer at the front, and the distance between rear bogie axle and leading coupled axle was reduced by 1½in. Frame length at the front did not have to be increased. One of these 6ft 6in side-bearer bogies weighed 5.43 tons complete.

TABLE II GENERAL DIMENSIONS OF BASIC JUBILEE TYPES (AS BUILT)

Locomotive numbers		5552–6	5557–5606	5642–6	5665–5742	Rebuilt 5735/6
Cylinders (3)	in	17 X 26	17 X 26	17 X 26	17 X 26	17 X 26
Wheel diam	in	81	81	81	81	81
Boiler pressure	psi	225	225	225	225	250
Bogie wheelbase	ft in	6–3	6–6	6–3	6–6	6–6
Engine wheelbase	ft in	27–5 1/2	27–7	27–5 1/2	27–7	27–7
No & od of tubes	in	160@2	160@2	130@2	159@1 7/8	198@1 3/4
No & od of flues	in	14@5 1/8	14@5 1/8	21@5 1/8	24@5 1/8	28@5 1/8
Free gas area	sq ft	3.9	3.9	4.1	4.55	4.94
Length between tube-plates	ft in	14–3	14–3	14–3	13–3	13–0
Evap h.s. — tubes & flues	sq ft	1463	1463	1372	1459	1667
firebox	sq ft	162	162	162	181	195
total	sq ft	1625	1625	1534	1640	1862
Type of firebox (1)		VT	VT	VT	ST	ST
Grate area	sq ft	29.5	29.5	29.5	31.0	31.25
Superheating surface	sq ft	228	228	256	307	357 (2)
Max axle load	tons	20.05 (3)	19.05	c.20	20.25	20.75
Adhesion weight	tons	59.75 (3)	56.95	c.60	60.0	61.5
Locomotive weight wo	tons	80.75 (3)	77.35	c.80	79.65	82.0
Locomotive weight empty	tons	75.35 (3)	70.35	c.73	73.27	75.9
Max height of loco	ft in	13–2 1/4	13–2 1/4	13–2 1/4	12–11 5/8	13–2 1/4
Tender type (4)		(a)	(d)	(c)	(d)	(d)
water capacity	gall	3,500	4,000	3,500	4,000	4,000
coal capacity	tons	5.5	9	7	9	9
tare	tons	21.5	27.95	26.9	27.95 (5)	26.8
laden weight	tons	42.7	54.65	49.6	54.65 (5)	53.65
Loco & tender wo weight	tons	123.45	132.0	129.6	134.3 (5)	135.65
Loco & tender wheelbase	ft in	52–3 1/4	54–4 3/4	52–3 1/4	54–4 3/4	54–4 3/4
Loco & tender over buffers	ft in	62–8	64–8 3/4	62–8	64–8 3/4	64–8 3/4
Tractive effort	lbs	26,610	26,610	26,610	26,610	29,590

(1) VT = vertical throatplate; ST = sloping throatplate. (2) Later 340 sq ft (3) Estimated weights
(4) See text for description. (5) Locomotives 5682/90 had welded tenders when new, 53.65 tons laden weight, 26.5 tons tare and 133.3 tons engine and tender weight.

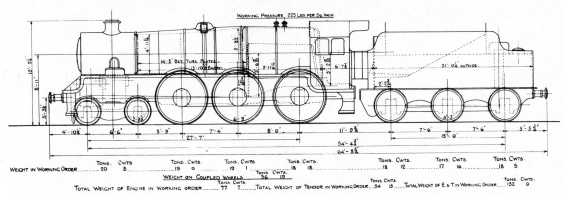

The lateral springs were set to 2.0 tons initial load, rising to 2.83 tons at the maximum travel of 2.25in per side.

Crewe-built engines Nos. 5552-56 and 5607-54 thus had 27ft 5½in locomotive wheelbase (Fig. 1); all the others had 27ft 7in (Fig. 2). These differences (see Table II) remained to the end, and so two different bogie types were always found in the class, but one was standard with that of the Patriots and the other was standard with that of hundreds of Class 5 4-6-0s and Class 4 2-6-4Ts. The 4000-gallon tender was 2ft longer than the 3500-gallon models, and so there were two length-over-buffer dimensions, and engine-

Left: **Fig 1** Diagram of first Crewe-built Jubilees of 27ft 5½in wheelbase and Fowler-type 3500-gallon tender; estimated weights given are actually the values of the preceding Patriots.

Above: **Fig 2** Diagram of NBL-built locomotives with vertical throatplate, 27ft 7in engine wheelbase, and Stanier-type 4000-gallon tender; actual weights given.

Below: One of the ten Derby-built Jubilees just after completion, with new-built Fowler-Stanier type of tender with 13ft 0in wheelbase. Leading bogie of side-bearer type. *(R. G. Jarvis collection)*

Bottom: The short-wheelbase central-pivot bogie and two smokebox saddles are well shown in this view of *Zanzibar* taken in June 1937 in its original condition, while standing at Cricklewood. *(H. C. Casserley)*

TABLE III BOILER DIMENSIONS TYPES 2A AND 3A (JUBILEE) AND 3B (BLACK FIVES) (1)

Boiler type	A	B	C	D	E
3A Vertical throatplate	5—0 (3)	5—8 3/8 (3)	14—3 (2)	13—9 15/16	6 3/8
3A Sloping throatplate	5—0	5—8 3/8	13—3 (2)	12—9 15/16	1—6 3/8
3B Vertical throatplate	4—11 11/16	5—8 1/2	14—3 (2)	13—9 15/16	6 7/16
3B Sloping throatplate	4—11 11/16	5—8 1/2	13—3 (2)	12—9 15/16	1—6 7/16
2A Sloping throatplate	5—5	5—10 1/2	13—0	12—6 11/16	1—9 5/8

(1) Dimensions in feet and inches; (2) Reduced by 1/8in when 1in copper tubeplate fitted 1938 onwards in place of 7/8in; (3) A = 4—11 11/16 and B = 5—7 5/8in. nickel-steel 3A type boilers (originally fitted to Nos 5557—5606).

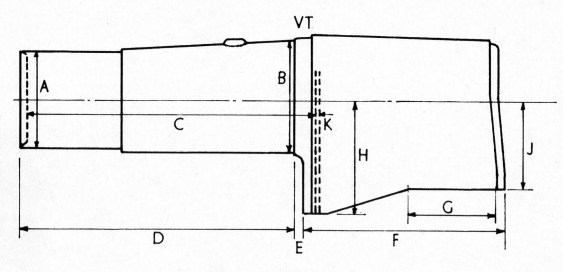

3A and 3B boilers

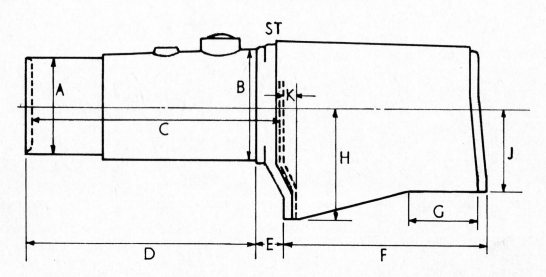

plus-tender wheelbase could be one of four values according to actual engine-and-tender combination (see tender description).

The original domeless vertical-throatplate boiler, with coning only on the top of the back ring, and known as the 3A, was built in mild steel and nickel steel versions which had trifling differences in inside and outside diameters at front and back. The nickel-steel 3A boilers were those built in Glasgow for the fifty NBL

Facing page: **Fig 3** Boiler diagram for dimensions of 3A (Jubilee) and 3B (Black Five) boilers. See also Table III.

F	G	H	J	K
10–0	4–5	5–6 7/8	4–2 7/8	Nil
10–0	3–1 3/4	5–6 7/8	4–2 7/8	10 1/2
9–2 13/16	3–9	5–6 7/16	4–2 7/16	Nil
9–2 13/16	2–2	5–6 7/16	4–2 7/16	10 9/16
10–3	c.3–4 1/2	5–7 3/8	4–2 3/8	1–1 3/4

locomotives; they had the same diameters and the same back ring as the nickel-steel 3B boilers fitted to all Black Fives. (For dimensions see Table III).

Possibly as the NBL Jubilees and first Black Fives were being built concurrently an attempt at standardisation was made, but later, as the first railway-built Jubilees came out lighter than the estimates, special means for weight-saving were unnecessary in subsequent engines, which reverted to the boiler sizes and materials of the first Crewe-built locomotives. All the 3A nickel-steel boilers had vertical throatplates and were interchangeable with the mild-steel 3A boilers of the same pattern, and both could be fitted to either the 27ft 5½in or 27ft 7in wheelbase.

Fireboxes of 3A (Jubilee) and 3B (Black Five) boilers were of quite different size, and so the complete nickel-steel boiler-firebox assemblies were not interchangeable between the two, though the barrel lengths were the same. At different stages firebox tubeplates, and the lengths, numbers and diameters of tubes and flues of 3A and 3B boilers also were the same, and the heating surface from those sources was then equal in the two classes.

As with other Stanier boilers of the time, the foundation ring was 3¾in wide, approaching the dimension tried experimentally by Churchward on the GWR in pre-1914 years and not pursued, as it gave no tangible benefit. Steam was collected by an up-turned mouth to the dry pipe, with a top opening about 13½in crossways and 1⅞in wide, located high up in the front of the outer firebox. The efficiency of this in entraining dry steam was helped by the big distance of 2ft between inner and outer firebox crowns. These details are shown in the outline of the vertical-throatplate box (Fig. 4a).

A sliding-type regulator was put in the smoke-box on the saturated-steam side of the superheater header, and had sight-feed lubrication. The top-feed casing, which simulated a small dome, was on the back ring of the boiler and housed two clackboxes. A continuous blow-

down valve was attached to the firebox and discharged beneath the tender through a ½in diameter pipe. A blow-off cock was put low down on the left-hand side of the firebox. The copper inside firebox was stayed in the breaking zone by Longstrand steel stays (NBL batch) and copper stays (railway-built boilers); other side stays were of steel. On top of the firebox were two 2½in pop

Below: **Fig 4a (top)** Outline of inside and outside fireboxes of vertical-throatplate 3A boiler.
Fig 4b (bottom) Outline of inside and outside fireboxes of sloping-throatplate 3A boiler.

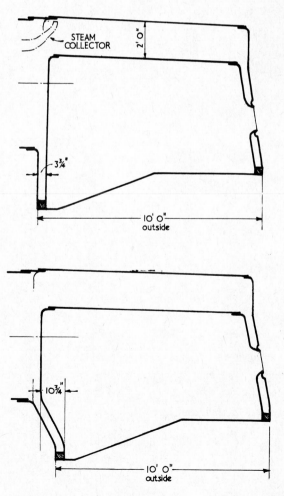

Left: Cab layout, showing lower-quadrant regulator handle, screw-reverse on left-hand side with combined vacuum-and-steam brake handle above it, steam manifold above the regulator sector, blower handle central between regulator sector and firedoor, exhaust-steam injector to right below footstep, and live-steam injector in corresponding position on left-hand side. *(Mitchell Library)*

Right: Jubilees under erection at Hyde Park, Glasgow. Boilers of domeless vertical-throatplate type, with forward half of grate sloped and backward half horizontal. Additional to the expansion angles on the firebox sides is a central boiler steadying bracket below the firedoor. *(Mitchell Library)*

Bottom right: **Fig 5** Diagram of Crewe-built sloping-throatplate 27ft 7in wheelbase Jubilees Nos. 5665-5742 with Stanier 4000-gallon tender.

safety-valves; those in the railway-built engines seem to have been of Ross type, but the NBL locomotives had the Auld make, supplied at a cost of £10 for the two on an engine.

Barrel and firebox were lagged with Alfol at a cost of 6½d/sq ft, and this lagging was encased in 12swg steel sheets. These cleading plates were to a uniform taper along the top from smokebox to firebox, a practice that gave rise to a widespread but erroneous belief that Stanier barrels had a continuous taper from front to back.

A steam manifold near the top of the firebox backplate, with a main shut-off valve and separate steam valves for vacuum-brake ejector,

steam brake, sight-feed lubricator, injectors, train heating, whistle and pressure-gauge was a feature that came new to the LMSR with Stanier, but it was inside the cab and not outside as in the USA and elsewhere, probably due to loading-gauge restrictions. The front end of the boiler was saddle-supported—the first application of this principle to an LMSR 4-6-0 and a big improvement over the horse-shoe tubeplate and built-up support in the Royal Scots and Patriots.

Similar early transition stages in the superheating of the 3A boilers of the Jubilees occurred as in the 3B boilers of the Class 5 engines and in the 3C/3D boilers of the Moguls and the No. 1

TABLE IV 3A BOILER HEATING SURFACE VARIATIONS JUBILEE CLASS 4—6—0

Foot note ref	Tubes No/Dia (inches)	Flues No/Dia (inches)	Heating surface sq ft	Superheater No/Dia (inches)	elements SWG	Superheating surface sq ft	Firebox heating surface sq ft	Grate area sq ft	Free gas area sq ft
(a)	160/2	14/5 1/8	1463	14/1 3/8	11	228	162	29.5	3.90
(b)	158/2	14/5 1/8	1447	14/1 3/8	11	228	162	29.5	3.88
(c)	130/2	21/5 1/8	1372	21/1 1/8	11	256	162	29.5	4.27
(d)	128/2	21/5 1/8	1357	21/1 1/8	11	256	162	29.5	4.25
(e)	168/2	21/5 1/8	1656	21/1 1/4	11	290	162	29.5	4.78
(f)	159/1 7/8	24/5 1/8	1570	24/1 1/4	11	331	162	29.5	4.55
(g)	138/2 1/8	21/5 1/8	1391	21/1 1/8	11	235	181	31.0	4.75
(h)	105/2 1/8	28/5 1/8	1270	28/1 1/8	11	312	181	31.0	4.80
(i)	168/1 7/8	21/5 1/8	1466	21/1 1/8	11	235	181	31.0	4.54
(j)	159/1 7/8	24/5 1/8	1459	24/1 1/4	11	307	181	31.0	4.55

Vertical throatplate boilers: notes (a) to (f).
Sloping throatplate boilers: notes (g) to (j).
(a) Nos 5552—5641, 5647—64 as built; (b) as (a) but number of tubes reduced by two; (c) Nos 5642—6 as built; (d) as (c) but number of tubes reduced by two; (e) boiler of No 5554 retubed; (f) boilers in (a) retubed and fitted with domes; (g) Nos 5665—76, 5678—5701 as built (some of these boilers may have had the number of tubes reduced by two). (h) No 5677 (this boiler retained this arrangement throughout its existence); (i) second boiler of No 5665 (built as spare and later altered to (j); (j) Nos 5702—42 as built: this became the standard arrangement for sloping throatplate boilers, but the boiler first fitted to No 5731 had 1in trifurcated elements with superheating surface of 357 sq ft for trial period.

boiler of the early Pacifics, and are detailed in Table IV. Nos. 5552-5641 and 5647-64 began life with fourteen flues of 5⅛in o.d., 160 steel tubes of 2in o.d., and fourteen sets of bifurcated elements of 1⅜in o.d. The boiler-firebox-smokebox assembly when so fitted weighed 17 tons dry with barrel and outer firebox plates of nickel steel.

Nos. 5642-46 marked the first modification in having twenty-one flues and a corresponding number of elements, and the number of 2in tubes was reduced to 130, and subsequently to 128 by replacing two of the tubes by two more washout plugs in the smokebox tubeplate. A single variation around this time was a complete rearrangement inside the barrel of No. 5554 whereby 168 tubes of 2in were crowded in along with 21 flues.

A final arrangement for vertical-throatplate 3A boilers was evolved in which 159 tubes of 1⅞in o.d. were used in conjunction with twenty-four flues of 5⅛in o.d. and 1¼in o.d. elements. Variations in superheating surface came with different element diameters and thicknesses in these and other 3A boilers, and are listed at the foot of Table XI (Chapter 4).

By the time that Nos. 5665-5742 were put in hand at Crewe these superheating developments were under way, and a re-design of the back end of the boiler to improve steaming capacity had been completed. Thus the first of the new sloping-throatplate domed 3A boilers (details in Tables III and IV) were put into these engines (Fig. 5). Those applied to Nos. 5665-76 and 5678-5701 when new were provided with twenty-one flues of 5⅛in diameter with 1⅛in

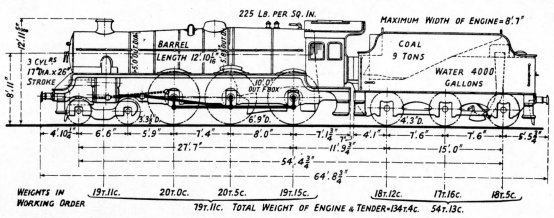

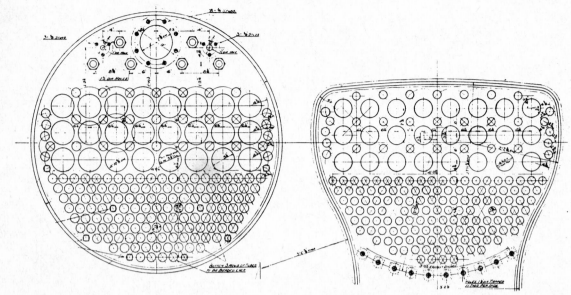

elements and 138 tubes of 2⅛in o.d.; superheating surface was only 235sq ft as the elements were shortened because of the reduced length between tubeplates. The unmentioned locomotive, No. 5677, was given a standard sloping-throatplate 3A boiler-firebox shell, but this contained twenty-eight flues and 105 tubes of 2⅛in o.d., and superheating surface was 312sq ft. This layout was retained throughout the boiler life. Another boiler, put on to No. 5665 rather later, was given 168 tubes of 1⅞in o.d. and twenty-one flues of 5⅛in o.d., but subsequently was altered to the final standard.

That standard was applied to Nos. 5702-42 as built, and the earlier sloping-throatplate boilers were altered to it as they became due for tube or tube-sheet renewals. Here, as in the vertical-throatplate boilers, 159 tubes of 1⅞in o.d. were combined with twenty-four flues of 5⅛in o.d. housing elements of 1¼in o.d., and free gas area was 4.55sq ft (see Fig. 6—due to E. S. Cox). Final steam temperature on long through runs seems to have averaged 550 to 580°F with this layout. As an exception, No. 5731 was given 1in trifurcated elements when new, distinct from the bifurcated type used in all the others, and it had a superheating surface of 357sq ft. Thus the 3A boilers as applied to the Jubilees, with the one exception first fitted to No. 5677, and which in time was on other engines in the class, never attained to the twenty-eight elements that from 1938 were standard in new 3B boilers for Class 5 engines.

By sloping the throatplate forward 10½in

from the foundation ring, the firebox in the 'revised' domed 3A boiler (see Fig. 4b) was given greater volume, and the heating surface was increased from 162sq ft to 181sq ft. Length between tubeplates also was reduced by 12in to 13ft 3in. Outer firebox length and width at grate level, and also the overall length of barrel and firebox, remained as before, but foundation ring width was reduced to 3in, and a result was a 5 per cent increase in grate area to 31sq ft. These increases in themselves brought greater evaporative capacity, which was supplemented by the effects of the 16 per cent larger free gas area through tubes and flues in the final layout compared with the original 14-flue plan.

In the sloping-throatplate domed 3A boiler the dome was put on the back, or tapered, ring; the top-feed was kept in the same position on the same ring but the clackboxes were covered with a narrower casing. A horizontal sliding regulator was housed in the dome at the highest possible level, about 5in higher than the old collector. The first Stanier domed boiler and new regulator had been put on the rebuild of the Class 6P 'special' No. 6170 *British Legion* that began to run in October 1935.

This dome-housed sliding regulator, in different sizes, henceforth became the LMSR standard. It had a pilot valve that opened first, but the approximate opening through the throttle could not be estimated simply by the position of the regulator handle in its movement up and down through a quarter of a circle between shut and fully open. This was because

Above: Crewe-built Jubilee of 1935 vintage rebuilt with domed boiler and 24-element superheater in place of the original domeless barrel and fourteen elements. Crosshead-driven vacuum pump removed; steam sanding has replaced the original gravity type, and a single saddle supports the smokebox in place of the two originals. Photograph taken at Bath in 1961, and shows driver W. Rawles, and Mr. Harold Morris, the last shedmaster at Bath Green Park. *(Ivo Peters)*

Left: **Fig 6** Final standard tube and flue layout for both forms of 3A boiler in the Jubilees; 24 flues, 159 tubes.

Below: **Fig 7** Graph of opening areas and handle positions, standard sliding-type regulator, Jubilee class. Solid line, opening; dotted line, closing.

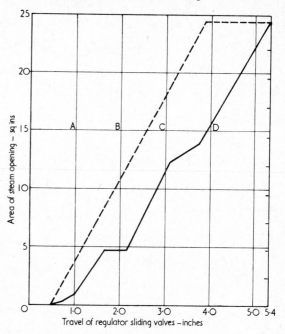

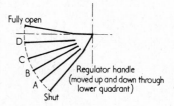

the proportionate areas open to steam were different when the valve was being opened from those when the valve was being closed. The areas at different positions and motions of the Jubilee regulator were as shown in Fig. 7. A gentle opening and quick closing were basic characteristics.

Minor modifications in the sloping-throatplate 3A boiler included six staggered washout plugs along each side of the outer firebox level with the inner crown, in place of the staggered five and six on the left-hand side and right-hand side on vertical-throatplate boilers. Two handholes also were put along the top curve of the outer box on each side and were staggered right and left. Firebox side stays in the breaking zone were of Monel metal. A supporting lip and plate on the smokebox door were put on many sloping-throatplate boilers, but were not on all. The snifting-valve and small casing on the left-hand side of the smokebox in the vertical-throatplate boilers were not found on the sloping pattern.

An interesting 1939 view of *Travancore*, built with domeless boiler and vertical-throatplate but altered in the frames to take the domed sloping-throatplate boiler shown; the two original smokebox saddles are retained. Chimney shorter than standard. Hand-sanding not yet replaced by steam. Vacuum pump removed but original crosshead retained. Speedometer newly fitted. *(D. G. Ritson collection)*

The vertical-throatplate boilers were never rebuilt to the sloping type. Those constructed with 14-element superheaters were gradually rebuilt from 1936 with domes, dome-housed regulators, 24-element superheaters and 159 small tubes. This work was finished by the end of 1940. Those vertical-throatplate boilers provided from the beginning with 21-element superheaters were never rebuilt, and remained domeless, with the regulator in the smokebox; but all vertical-throatplate variations were inter-changeable over the number group 5552-5664, and so the five boilers that remained domeless could be on different engines from time to time. Handholes along the top of the firebox sides were not added when the boilers were given domes.

Vertical- and sloping-throatplate types were not interchangeable, for the frame structure of the former locomotives could not take the second type of boiler without alteration. The two were readily distinguishable to outside view in that the boiler-firebox joint of the sloping-throatplate version was above the driving-wheel centre, and 10in behind that centre in the vertical-throatplate type.

No spare boilers of the vertical-throatplate pattern were built. To provide spares, eight boilers were withdrawn in 1936-37 to form a pool, and new boilers of the sloping-throatplate type were built under separate orders to take their place. The frames of the engines affected were altered by moving forward the cast-steel cross-stay just in front of the throatplate and modifying the rear dragbox to take a different steadying bracket. Actually eleven locomotives

were altered, Nos. 5567/90, 5607/8/10/6/21/2/ 39/40/57; but three (all originally with mild steel boilers) carried the sloping-throatplate boiler only a short time before reverting to the original type (see footnotes (2) and (3), Table IX).

New sloping-throatplate boilers to cover the above and to act as spares for the last seventy-eight Jubilees were built to separate orders for six and seven in 1936-38 and for one in 1941. Thus in the end the boiler total was 205 for 191 locomotives, and from 1942 was made up of: (*a*) 108 vertical-throatplate domeless boilers rebuilt with domes, fifty of which were in nickel steel; (*b*) five domeless vertical-throatplate boilers not rebuilt; (*c*) seventy-eight sloping-throatplate domed boilers built for locomotive orders; and (*d*) fourteen sloping-throatplate domed boilers built as spares or replacements.

Crewe constructed all the boilers for the railway-built Jubilees, including those for the ten built at Derby, and all the spares. These were of normal boiler steel and not the alloy steel of the NBL batch. The cost of the latter material was hardly a deterring factor, for the nickel-steel plates for barrel and outer firebox cost only £138 per engine rough, or about £16.50 per ton. The nickel steel saved about 1¼ tons per engine. For the fifty NBL locomotives Queen's Park built the boilers only for works numbers 24144-59 (LMSR Nos. 5586-5601); the other thirty-four boilers were built at Hyde Park.

As built, the vertical-throatplate engines, Nos. 5552-5664, had the front end of the boiler supported on two smokebox saddles. The front one was integral with the inside-cylinder casting and was of iron; the rear saddle was inboard of the outside steam pipes and was of cast steel, and was prolonged downwards to act as a stay between the outside cylinders. With Nos. 5665-5720 a single large cast-steel saddle was introduced, and it was not part of the inside-cylinder casting. Nos. 5721-42 had a slight

variation in the single saddle. The single saddle could be distinguished by three strengthening ribs on each side forward of the steampipe casing. This single saddle in the form applied to Nos. 5721-42 was very gradually from 1938 put on the 113 earlier double-saddle engines, but the change was not allied specifically to other boiler alterations.

Jubilee smokeboxes were 7ft 4in long and 5ft 4in diameter, and originally were fitted with the inside sloping ash deflector plate then common in Stanier locomotives and shown in Fig. 8. At first the blast nozzle was 5⅛in diameter and set 7⅛in below boiler centre line and 33⅝in below a choke of 15in diameter; it had a Churchward jumper top and the blower was arranged round the choke. Chimney centre line was 3in forward of the outside steampipe, but in line with the bogie pivot.

Outside cylinders 17in by 26in were set at a slope of 1 in 50, but the inside cylinder, set far forward, was horizontal and drove through a connecting rod much shorter than the outside pair on to the leading coupled axle, which was of built-up form with 5in balanced webs and an 8¼in by 5½in centre crankpin. Ratios of connecting-rod length to crank throw were 1:6.3 inside and 1:9.7 outside. The inside crosshead, piston-rod glands, rear cylinder cover and rear valve-chest cover were difficult of access and collected much dirt. The outside cylinders drove the centre pair of coupled wheels through connecting rods 11ft 6in long; nevertheless the complete inside rod at 476lb scaled a few pounds more than the longer outside rod, mainly because of the heavier big-end and brasses encircling the large inside pin. Compared with the Patriots the cylinder diameter was reduced one inch in view of the 25lb/sq in higher boiler pressure.

Mechanically the weak spot of the Jubilees was the inside big-end, and even before the war a stink bomb had to be tried to give drivers some warning of a hot bearing. This was a 1in phial

Above: One of the last seventy-eight Crewe-built Jubilees, to all of which the sloping-throatplate boiler was fitted. By the time No. 5684 was completed the Jubilees were being named, and many engines came out new with names. Trickle sanding was continued on these engines up to No. 5694. Single smokebox saddle in place of two saddles in the first 113 engines.

Right: **Fig 8** Original smokebox layout of Jubilees, 1934-36 but with reduced nozzle diameter.

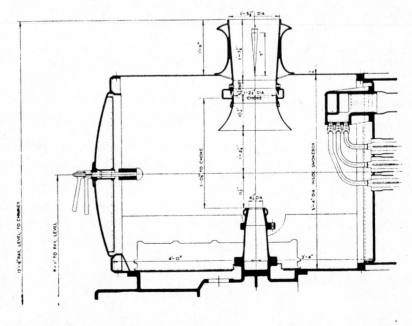

Above: Front end of sloping-throatplate engine, showing 1936 sans numerals applied to cast iron number plate on smokebox door. The lip and catch at the side of the door were not fitted to all Jubilees. No steam-heating connection was fitted to the front of these locomotives. *(R. T. Ellis collection)*

Below: **Fig 9** Section through the Stanier cast-steel axlebox with pressed-in brass and serrated whitemetal lining; slide-out keep below.

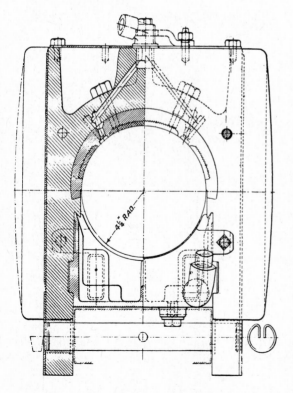

containing a garlic solution let into one of the split brasses and sealed with a small lead cap. The last-named fused if the bearing ran hot and released the garlic. This inside big-end weakness was never wholly overcome; and in 1948 a report to British Railways recorded that over the preceding seven years the 189 Jubilees (that is 191 minus the two that had been rebuilt in 1942) had averaged twenty-four inside big-end failures a year, and some of these had led to much consequential damage such as breakage of the inside-cylinder casting. Distinct from the four-cylinder Pacifics and two-cylinder Class 5 4-6-0s and Class 8F 2-8-0s, the three-cylinder Jubilees did not have Stanier's normal 28in stroke for main-line engines, because of the crank axle and its clearances.

Three sets of Walschaerts motion actuated piston valves of the unusual diameter of 10⅝in, meaning 62.7 per cent of the cylinder bore, one of the largest ratios ever used in British practice. The inside set was driven by a single eccentric on the right-hand side of the leading single-crank axle, and gave a maximum travel of 6⅛in, corresponding to about 77 per cent cut-off. The outside valves had a maximum travel of 6⅜in, and were driven by well-proportioned motion with nearly equal eccentric and radius rod lengths—80.1in and 72.125in respectively, and with a 15.156in flycrank.

The valve heads were sealed by the six narrow rings per head adopted on the LMSR some two years before Stanier's arrival, but in the Jubilees for some reason, while these gave satisfactory sealing, the valve heads themselves at first wore unduly. The inside piston valve was 8in to the right of its cylinder and 17⅝in above it. The outside cylinders were spaced transversely at 6ft 8⅝in and their piston valves at 7ft 3⅝in; piston valve centres were 19in higher than cylinder centre line.

Reversing was by screw in the left-hand side of the cab, and the reach rod had an intermediate support on the running plate between the second and third splashers. From the main reversing shaft a subsidiary reach rod ran forward on the right-hand side between the frame to a short cross shaft for the inside motion.

Frame thickness nominally was $1\frac{1}{16}$in, but the main frame plates ordered from Colville for the NBL engines were $1\frac{3}{32}$in, and cost only £43.50 per locomotive. Cross-stays of cast steel were fitted between the horns of the second and third coupled wheel pairs. Between firebox and inside cylinder the frame was further stayed by four steel castings, but the Jubilee framing did not have the excellent racking stays that were a feature of the Royal Scots.

The cast steel axleboxes (Fig. 9) with pressed-in brasses were one of Stanier's major contributions to LMSR locomotive performance, and in the Jubilees, possibly because of the more even turning moment from three cylinders, gave the best results of all, for these engines up to 1940 needed axlebox repairs at an average of 95,500 miles, whereas the four-cylinder stream-lined Pacifics came in for that purpose at 90,800 miles average and the Royal Scots at only 63,500 miles. The Jubilees shared in the record of all taper-boiler engines with these boxes built from 1932 in averaging only one hot box per engine in the first six years or more. Through 1939 around 7,500 coupled boxes of this form on the LMSR suffered only 122 hot boxes, contrasted with 1,140 from about 10,000 of the old Midland bronze type in 1931, but the 1939 proportion was not quite so good as that of 1938 when out of about 6,700 coupled boxes only 89 'hots' occurred.

In all Jubilees as built the white metal journal lining was serrated into the brass, but in later years the serrations were given up and plain bonding of the ⅛in metal substituted. Lubricating oil was introduced at the low-pressure location at the axle centre line and led upwards to the bearing surface. Another feature was a

This view outside the NBL Hyde Park works well shows the eight pipe leads from the cylinder-valvechest mechanical lubricator; also to the fore are the two smokebox saddles, the water drain pipe from the vacuum brake ejector exhaust pipe, and (below the smokebox door), the short casing over the front of the inside valve spindle. *(Mitchell Library)*

felt pad that lubricated the side thrust face of the wheel boss. A complete coupled axlebox for a Jubilee weighed 428lb. Because of the crank-webs and eccentric the slide-out keep of the standard axlebox could not be applied to the front coupled boxes.

Though Stanier was accustomed on the GWR to hydrostatic or sight-feed lubrication of cylinders and valves, made practicable by the low final steam temperature given by the Swindon superheater, the LMSR practice of mechanical lubrication was adopted for the Jubilees, with a 16-feed Silvertown lubricator on the left-hand running plate for the three pistons and piston valves plus their respective glands. Four rams were spare. This lubricator was driven from the left-hand combination lever. On the right-hand side running plate was a similar eight-feed lubricator supplying oil to the coupled boxes, and this was driven off the right-hand combination lever. On Nos. 5552-5654 atomisation of the lubricating oil to pistons and valves was controlled by pumps in the lubricator, but No. 5655 *et seq* had steam atomisation controlled from the cylinders. From 1939 the first 103 engines were converted to the second system.

As with all Stanier's engines, the coupled wheels of the Jubilees had rigid triangular-section rims and 3in tyres with 1 in 20 tread taper, secured by Gibson rings. This combination, which was under development on the LMSR when Stanier arrived and gave it greater impetus, almost eliminated tyre failures. Previously there had been seventeen or eighteen failures a year. In the Jubilees the tyres were given their last re-turning when a thickness of 2in was reached, and were removed for scrapping when down to 1⅞in, that is, when the new tread diameter of 6ft 9in was down to 6ft 6¾in. The leading coupled wheel-and-axle set when new weighed 4.68 tons; the centre set weighed just half a ton less.

Part of the tyre improvement scheme was the suppression of cast-in balance weights and the substitution of separate steel side plates riveted together round the spokes and with a lead insert of the correct amount; this method was a visible feature of all Stanier locomotives. As a rule the side plates remained the original size whatever balancing proportion might be tried later.

Reciprocating weight for each of the three drive lines of the Jubilees was 750 lb, and two-thirds was balanced in the wheels. The revolving weights of the inside line were balanced by prolongation of the crank webs. The whole amount of the reciprocating balance was divided equally between the six coupled wheels. As the forces in the left-hand and right-hand sides were nearly opposite, there were small hammer blows per axle and for the whole engine but large blows per wheel and per rail, the values at 5 revs/sec (72mph) being 3.06 tons/wheel, 0.23 tons/axle, 8.31 tons/rail and 0.61 tons/engine.

Trickle sanding to the front of the first and second pairs of coupled wheels and to the back of the second pair in Nos. 5552-5694 was replaced by steam sanding to the same points in Nos. 5695-5742 when new, after strong recommendations in 1936 by the operating department. This resuscitated pre-Stanier LMSR custom, for the hand sanding was a GWR practice brought over from Swindon in 1932. Automatic water de-sanders front and back of the coupled wheel group in the first 113 engines were not fitted to the next seventy-eight, and were removed from the earlier engines from 1938 onwards.

A steam brake cylinder secured to the dragbox below the cab floor operated a single block on the front of each coupled wheel, and was applied by movement of the driver's vacuum brake handle, so that proportional application was made in conjunction with the continuous brakes of the train, or separately if the engine was running light or at the head of an unbraked freight. The Jubilees were never fitted with double brake blocks as were Class 5 locomotives built 1938 onwards, but the number of unbraked freight trains they handled was much fewer, though fitted freights were found in several pre-war rosters.

All Class 5XP engines when built had a 5in vacuum pump driven off the left-hand crosshead, a feature dating back to Webb on the LMSR constituents and to Dean's time at Swindon, and one which had been prominent on the Royal Scots in 1927. This took the place of the small ejector in maintaining sufficient vacuum to keep the brakes off while running. Through the years 1938-41 these pumps were removed gradually from LMSR locomotives that had them, including all the Jubilees, for a normal small ejector was found to do the work equally well on a smaller steam consumption than calculated in the 1920s, and the pumps had required rather more maintenance and shed inspection than had been anticipated. From

1945 the Gresham & Craven driver's brake valves on Nos. 5552-5664 were replaced by LMSR standard valves, which Nos. 5665-5742 had had from new.

Official diagrams for the first fifty-three Crewe-built engines of 27ft 5½in wheelbase gave only what were claimed to be estimated weights grossing 80.75 tons in working order, with 20.05 tons maximum axle load, and a weight of 75.3 tons empty; but actually no reasoned estimate was made, and the weights and distribution on the diagram were simply the actual values of the then newly-built Patriots. No revised diagram giving actual weights was ever published, and, as far as can be traced, ever prepared.

When the first NBL locomotives, of 27ft 7in wheelbase and with vertical-throatplate boilers, were completed the published weight, as released by the LMSR in October 1934, was 79.55 tons in working order. This total weight, along with a maximum axle load of 20.25 tons and an adhesion weight of 60 tons, was given also in the official diagram of 1936 for the first sloping-throatplate engines, and this diagram continued in use thereafter through LMSR days, though obviously the weights could not have been the same as those published for the NBL engines. The latter engines, indeed, were not to any of these weights, for NBL records show that the engine working order weight was only 77.35 tons, the adhesion weight 56.95 tons, and the empty weight 70.35 tons, values never found in any LMSR diagrams or releases. The weight of 79.55 tons presumably was the actual value of the 27ft 5½in wheelbase vertical-throatplate locomotives. A ton or more of the difference could have come from the use of nickel steel for barrel and outer firebox plates in the Glasgow-built locomotives. NBL working order weights were with 7 cwt of coal on the firegrate, and with the boiler containing cold water to 2⅞in above the gauge cock, which meant 2½in showing in the gauge glass when heated to working pressure. Equivalent under LMSR weighing conditions would have been about 78 tons total.

Early 'Red Staniers', as the Jubilees were known occasionally from the summer of 1934 to distinguish them from the Black Staniers or Black Fives, appeared in LMSR red with the type of insignia introduced in 1928, with 12in numerals on the cabsides and 14in letters *LMS* on the tender sides at 40in spacing. In a few of the earliest deliveries the lettering on the

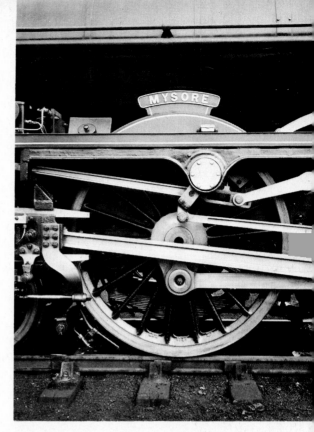

Arm-and-rod drive of vacuum pump from left-hand crosshead. When the pumps were removed the crosshead was unaltered, and many engines ran for years with the blank face and six bolt holes. This picture also shows clearly the trickle sanding pipe, and clipped to it the front hot-water de-sander, the webbed spokes supporting the crank boss, and the original 12-plate underhung laminated spring. Oilbox below nameplate is for lubrication of the expansion-link trunnion. *(British Railways)*

Fowler-type tenders was set slightly to the rear end of the tank side sheets, but later was centred in both 3500-gallon and 4000-gallon tenders.

Black-and-yellow lining was applied to the running angle, back and front of the cylinder and valve-chest casings, splashers, footsteps, front end of boiler barrel, and firebox-cab angle. Some of the 1934-35 engines of railway build and all of NBL build had lining all round the cab sides and base, and turned in at the top as far as the side windows; otherwise there was no lining along the top edge. Power classification *5XP* was in 2½in characters just below the cabside windows. Buffer beams were vermilion with black-and-yellow lining. Letters and numerals were of scroll and serif form. Wheel rims, axle ends, and smokebox hinges were finished bright and unpainted, as in other Stanier engines of the 1930s.

Before the end of the last bulk delivery (Nos. 5665-5742) the scroll and serif insignia had been changed for new engines and repaints, as from February 1936, to a sans type, and certainly from No. 5721, if not before, this was applied to new Jubilees in 10in gold-leaf red-shaded numerals on the cab sides, and in similar 14in lettering *LMS* centred on the tender sides. Sans numbers also were used for the cast iron smokebox door plates, and for the 2in *5XP* transfer below the cab windows. Few of the earlier engines were changed to this new form, for at the beginning of 1938 the LMSR announced a reversion to the old scroll and serif style, but with vermilion shading.

From 1938 yellow in place of gold leaf was used for repaints, thought not to a great extent, for from 1940, owing to war conditions, Class 5XP complete repaints to 1945 were unlined black with yellow unshaded letters and numbers; a few exceptions had red-shaded insignia. However, not many Class 5XPs were more than patch-painted during the war years, while some managed to retain the last pre-1940 red repaint throughout, and no fewer than ten were actually given their BR five-figure numbers on the red background paint of 1939-40.

The lined black livery adopted by the LMSR in 1946 was applied to many Jubilees. On the glossy black base was put maroon and straw lining along the running angle, cylinder and valve-chest casing, and cabsides, and the tenders had lining all round the sides. Buffer beams were unlined vermilion. Locomotive number was in unshaded 12in sans, with 2½in power-classification insignia below it. The 14in *LMS* on tenders was straw-coloured with maroon lining all round. Afterwards lining bands were put round front and rear of the boiler barrel and over the firebox-cab angle on many engines.

Prior to the adoption of the 1946 livery, No. 5573 *Newfoundland* was painted experimentally in blue-grey with broad maroon edging and lining, and with *5XP* below the numerals. At the same time No. 5594 *Bhopal* was repainted LMSR red and was given the pre-war black edging and gold lining except on the splashers—according to one report on one side only. Both engines had unshaded yellow sans insignia. No. 5573 soon was repainted to 1946 black standard, but *Bhopal* ran in red for several years, and was actually the last engine to be given a new red livery by the LMSR. It had the number rather low on the cab side, with the *5XP* classification below.

Until the BR livery was determined, a hybrid appeared when early in 1948 the prefix *M* was put on Nos. 5575, 5602/6/25/51/3/6/61/73/81/2/6/93 and 5714/27/38; the tenders were lettered BRITISH RAILWAYS. Smokebox number plates were altered to conform, even to the extent of casting new number plates with the prefix *M*. Later the 40000 was added to all numbers and a few engines were painted experimental colours. Nos. 45565, 45604 and 45694 appeared in light green, fully-lined in red, grey and black with pale straw insignia; No. 45709 and a few others were turned out in the lined-black later adopted for mixed-traffic classes. The final chosen livery was GWR Brunswick green with black-orange-black lining, 8in sans numerals in off-white, and the lion-and-wheel emblem.

Apart from a change of emblem in 1957 that livery remained standard, other than the individualistic use of 12in numerals by St Rollox for Scottish-based engines, until in the last few years of steam life repaints were in unlined green, and often with nameplates removed. In September 1964 all Jubilees still in service had a 5in wide diagonal yellow stripe painted on each cab side to indicate prohibition from working over electrified lines south of Crewe.

Names were not given to the first 113 engines on introduction. The first name was *Silver Jubilee,* bestowed in April 1935 in commemora-

tion of the 25 years' reign of King George V. This name was actually put on Crewe works number 205 which ran for three or four months previously in red with its true running number, 5642; the desire was to associate the name with the whole class, and No. 5642 therefore exchanged numbers with the first Jubilee of all, No. 5552, and these renumberings remained until the end.

Silver Jubilee first appeared bearing the name at an exhibition of rolling stock on 2 and 3 May 1935. After the naming proposals were sanctioned in March the time had been occupied in giving No. 5642 (original) an entirely different exterior finish, the red being replaced by highly varnished black, with a 'silver lining' effect gained by chrome-plating of the handrails and pillars, boiler clothing bands, window beading, smokebox door handles and hinges, ejector pipe connection on smokebox side, the main reach

Top left: The first Jubilee to be painted with the then (1936) new sans insignia; this was applied new to all succeeding engines, and given to any earlier Jubilees that had complete repaints until 1938. *(British Railways)*

Top: One of the domeless vertical-throatplate engines rebuilt with dome and larger superheater, painted in the wartime black with unshaded letters and numerals, but in this case with maroon lining along the running angle and on cab and tender. This engine still running with two smokebox saddles. *(R. T. Ellis collection)*

Above: Sloping-throatplate engine in LMSR standard black livery of 1946, with shaded insignia, and lining on boiler-firebox division. Ulster Red Hand plaque above the name plate. Power-classification transferred below cabside numerals. *(J. B. Radford collection)*

Below: In experimental light green livery with red, grey and black lining and pale straw insignia, as turned out early in 1948 before final choice of BR colour scheme. Stanier 4000-gallon welded tender attached. *(British Railways)*

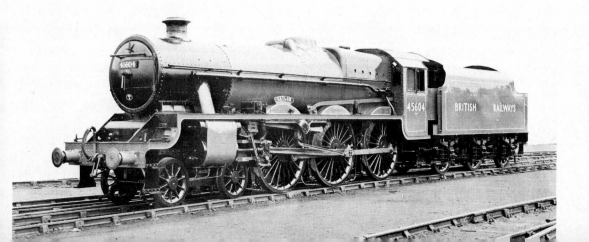

Above: The second No. 5552 (originally 5642) painted in high-gloss black with chromium-plated raised insignia and details, after naming in April 1935. The tender is neither that of the original 5552 nor of the original 5642, but is a Stanier-type 4000-gallon unit that came off No. 5559. *(D. G. Ritson collection)*

Below right: Broadside of one of the first five Jubilees as built, with domeless vertical-throatplate boiler, 6ft 3in bogie wheelbase and 27ft 5½in locomotive wheelbase. Old-standard 3500-gallon tender. *(National Railway Museum)*

rod, and even the top-feed casing. The raised numbers on the cab sides and smokebox door, and the raised letters *LMS* on the tender, were cut from $\frac{5}{16}$ in steel plate and given a chromium finish, and the brass nameplates were also so treated. This process was carried out *in situ* by a spraying method that prevented peeling and stripping in service. Most of the work was done at Crewe, but some details were finished at Camden depot, in each case by employees of the Chromium Portable Plater Sales Co. In June and July the engine made an exhibition tour over parts of the Midland and Central Divisions.

This finish, in varying degrees of cleanliness, lasted through the war years, but in mid-1945 the numbers and letters were painted white. The black base colour remained until the engine was given a coat of BR green in the early 1950s, and even then the engine did not at once get the five-figure BR numeral 45552 in chromed figures. Towards the end of its life, after some months in store at Crewe, when taken out in October 1963 to head an enthusiasts' special over the Western Region, some of the chromed numbers had disappeared, and were replaced by wooden cut-outs painted over.

From the naming of the new No. 5552 in April 1935 the class gradually became known as the Jubilee under official aegis, and later that year further engines received names, but not at all in the order of construction. In January 1936, at the time No. 5665 was named, a list of names for the first 179 engines was issued, and names for Nos. 5731-42 were selected before those engines were completed. All engines had nameplates by early 1938, and the names generally were those of Dominions and their provinces or states,

Crown Colonies, famous admirals and well-known naval battles, but eight of the last series built (Nos. 5731-38) were given names of celebrated pioneer locomotives that hitherto had been carried by Royal Scots.

Names are included in Table IX, which gives the full list of Jubilees with delivery and withdrawal dates. Only a few engines went through naming ceremonies, eg No. 5595 on 27 May 1937 and No. 5564 on 26 January 1938, in each case after carrying the nameplates in service for some months. Five engines, Nos. 5572, 5610, 5616, 5633 and 5700 also had a change of name or a modification in their time. No. 5700 became *Amethyst* in September 1951 after running nameless since January 1951 when the first BR Britannia Pacific appeared. *Amethyst* was selected to commemorate the exploit of the frigate of that name on the Yangtse in 1949. No. 5739 *Ulster* was given in 1947 plaques of the Red Hand to go above the nameplates.

Nameplates were cast brass with the letters polished and the background black. They were carried above the leading splashers. Seven or eight sets are believed to have been cast at St Rollox works for engines already working on the Northern Division at the time names were selected. Works plates (oval cast-iron for railway build, circular brass for Hyde Park and diamond-form brass for Queen's Park) were attached to the frames in front of the running plate drop.

No fewer than four tender types were attached to the Jubilees as the locomotives came new out of the shops, though the tenders themselves were by no means all new. These types were, in LMSR nomenclature of the time:

    (*a*) Old standard straight sides, 3,500 gallons, 5½ tons coal.

    (*b*) Modified old standard, higher straight sides, 3,500 gallons, 7 tons coal.

    (*c*) New type, higher sides with in-curving top edge, 3,500 gallons, 7 tons coal.

    (*d*) Stanier type, curved-top sides, 4,000 gallons, 9 tons coal.

The actual original tender attachments were:

    Type (a) Locomotives 5552-56: new-built tenders Nos. 4559-63; Locomotives 5695-99, 5700-25, 5740: all transferred from Royal Scots as Jubilees were completed.

    Type (b) Locomotives 5607-16: tender Nos. 4564-73.

    Type (c) Locomotives 5617-66: tender Nos. 4600-49.

    Type (d) Locomotives 5557-5606, 5667-94, 5728-37: all new-built tenders; 5726-27, 5738-39, 5741-42: transferred from Princess Royal Pacifics when the latter got 10-ton coal tenders during the time the later Jubilees were being built.

Original allocations and subsequent re-allocations of Jubilee tenders extending over many years were complicated in the extreme, and a 'history' of these is given in an appendix; but mention may be made here that out of the original allocations given above the Crewe-built tenders for locomotives Nos. 5617-36 were built to Crewe order number T391, and those for locomotives Nos. 5637-54 to a further Crewe order, number T392. In neither case was any locomotive included in the order. From the original allocations given above the NBL engines are seen to have had their Glasgow-built Stanier-type tenders, which bore LMSR tender numbers 9004-53; many of these were soon exchanged for old-standard 3,500-gallon tenders off Royal Scots (see Appendix, Table B).

Surprise has sometimes been expressed at the number of Jubilees given 3,500-gallon tenders. Apart from the desire to give the more powerful Royal Scots the bigger tenders, Stanier himself had reported to the Locomotive Committee in April 1932 that 3,500 gallons was the best quantity for general purposes, but for longer runs or heavier haulage than found at that time larger tenders would be advisable. The last proviso led to the 4,000-gallon model.

As fitted to the Patriots and Jubilees the old-standard tender (*a*), a Fowler type, had low sides with two coal rails along the top. The modified old-standard type (*b*), also basically a Fowler, had much heightened straight sides, no coal rails, and very high curved bunker end plates reaching to 12ft 4in above rails, to give a heaped coal capacity of 7 tons. Earliest *published* photographs of the original No. 5552 (May-June 1934) show a type (*b*) tender attached, but the official photographs of Nos. 5552-56 taken at the time show type (*a*). Only ten tenders of type (*b*) were constructed.

The new type of category (*c*) was a mixture of Fowler and Stanier practices, with the old short wheelbase and Stanier's in-curving tops to the sides, and the end curves were concave to the tank top instead of the old convex. These tenders also had the high bunker end plates and a self-trimming floor. Tank capacity was still given as 3,500 gallons though the tanks were wider and almost in line with the cab sides. In fact, this tender could not be distinguished readily from the Stanier 4,000-gallon type (*d*) despite the shorter wheelbase.

Type (*d*) weighed 27.5 tons empty according to railway records and 27.95 tons according to NBL data, but the fully-laden weight was always given as 54.65 tons for riveted tenders. Nos. 5682/90 were given early in 1936 what were definitely the first railway-built welded tenders (Nos. 9153/61) and these scaled 53.65 tons full.

The so-called Fowler 3,500-gallon types (*a*)

Above left: Rear end of Fowler old-standard 3500-gallon tender, train-heating hose below buffer beam. *(Reed collection)*

Above right: Front end of Stanier 4000-gallon tender of riveted construction. Intermediate drawbar with two safety bars and with two light sprung intermediate buffers. *(Mitchell Library)*

and (*b*), along with type (*c*), had 13ft 0in wheelbase and the same total frame length of 20ft 8in; and when attached the overall length of engine and tender was 62ft 8¾in. Engine-plus-tender wheelbase was 52ft 3½in or 52ft 5in according to the wheelbase of the locomotive attached. Stanier tender wheelbase was 15ft, and overall length of engine and tender 64ft 8¾in. Engine-plus-tender wheelbase was 54ft 3¼in or 54ft 4¾in.

Both Fowler and Stanier types had 51in 12-spoke wheels with a single brake block against the rear face of each wheel, applied by a single vertical cylinder at the front. Up to 1933 all Fowler-type LMSR tenders had countersunk rivet heads in tank and bunker, but Stanier favoured snap-head rivets and these were applied to those Fowler-type tenders (*a*) and (*b*) built new for the Jubilees.

The Stanier tender was wider, 8ft 6in against 7ft 1in, and had the characteristic in-curving top edge to the ⅜in tank side plates that brought the sides in to a 7ft coal gap on top. Also it had much more effective self-trimming properties,

TABLE V DIMENSIONS TENDERS ATTACHED TO JUBILEE CLASS LOCOMOTIVES

Type Model Reference in text			Old standard (Fowler) (a)	3500 gal Modified (b)	New (c)	4000 gal Stanier (d)
Wheel diam		in	51	51	51	51
Wheelbase (1)	ft	in	13—0	13—0	13—0	15—0
Coal capacity		tons	5.5	7.0	7.0	9.0
Water capacity		gal	3,500	3,500	3,500	4,000
Tare		tons	21.5	21.6	26.9	27.5/27.9 (2)
Full weight		tons	42.7	44.3	49.6	54.65 (2)

(1) Equally divided; (2) Rivetted tender; welded model weighed one ton less.

One of the ten Fowler-modified tenders (type *b* in text) with high straight sides, built in 1934 and attached first to Nos. 5607-16. Running in July 1959 behind No. 45568. The train is the Thames-Clyde Express, running that day without headboards.

with the bunker floor plate at an angle of 22½ degrees to the horizontal and extending almost to the rear of the tender. The 18½in tank filling hole at the rear was reached by angle-iron footsteps up each side of the back plate. That end also carried a rectangular cast-iron plate giving the LMSR tender number and construction date, and above this was an oval plate showing the water capacity. The outside plain-bearing axle journals were 7½in diameter by 10⅝in long, and each axlebox, carried in 1in frames, weighed 326lb. Hand-brake and water-scoop handles were similar, with shafts sloping slightly down from the horizontal and with bevel-gear application. The former was on the right and the scoop handle on the left.

The brake on the tender, which had a single steam cylinder of its own, was applied by the handle movement of the driver's brake valve and could not be used independently of the locomotive brake. A hand brake on the tender was actuated through a wheel on an inclined shaft.

Change of tender type was not simply a matter of uncoupling one and coupling-up the substitute when different classes were involved. Adjustments were needed to intermediate drawbars and buffers, and liners had to be inserted to reduce tender brake cylinder diameter when taking a tender from a 225 lb/sq in Jubilee and attaching it to a Royal Scot working at 250 lb/sq in. Type (*a*) also continued to give trouble by buffer-locking.

Of all Stanier's engines, the Jubilees had the worst reputation for indifferent and erratic steaming. Especially was this so with the 14-flue layout. Very quickly some improvement had to be made, and the blast nozzle was reduced to 4⅞in and even to 4¾in diameter in the 14-flue boilers and to 5in in the 21-flue type and 4⅞in with 24 flues. Then from around 1937 the jumper top was removed; a parallel-bore chimney liner was tried on some engines to reduce the choke diameter, in place of the original 1 in 7 taper; the blower was then removed to the blastpipe top. The ash

Above: Fuelling a Stanier tender with nine tons of coal in 1936 from Preston mechanical coaling plant, then not long erected. *(Reed collection)*

Below: This sloping-throatplate engine was fitted with Kylchap double exhaust in 1937 and ran so equipped for nearly twelve months before reconversion to normal in 1938. *(National Railway Museum)*

deflector-plates were taken out, often un-officially at first; and attempts to flatten the firegrate were made by raising the bars at the front and dropping them at the centre.

The 24-flue layout, sloping-throatplate fire-box, and greater free gas area through tubes and flues really cured all the troubles, and in that type of firebox the grate itself had a longer and gentler slope over two-thirds of the length and a shorter level section at the back, and the free air space between the bars amounted to 40 per cent of the grate area. The revised single-saddle front support also was said to help steaming, as there had been some air leaks into the smokebox through bolt breakages and the slightly different 'working' of the two saddles and their bolts.

Perhaps the Jubilees were always a little more sensitive to poor handling than the Black Fives, and the early reputation had a lingering death, particularly among crews who tended to shovel coal through the firedoor in large doses. Little-and-often firing with a thin bed gave consistent good steaming, adequate superheat and fast running, with a distinctive exhaust 'roar' when working hard.

Some of the early troubles of the first engines were due in part to the small superheater that on occasion when working hard had to act first as an evaporator, and which could not give enough superheat. In fact, final steam temperature rarely seems to have got above 500-510°F with 14-element boilers. In addition, the flow area through the neck of the bifurcated elements was smaller than the area through the steam intake, dry pipe and less than that through the full-open regulator, so that steam was wiredrawn in passing through the superheater. As hinted earlier, the free gas area through tubes and flues (3.9sq ft, or 13.2 per cent of the grate area in the

14-flue boilers) also was on the small side. The smokebox regulator wore comparatively quickly on slide and seat, perhaps because of difficulty in maintaining continuous adequate sight-feed lubrication; and that was a contributory reason for putting domes on the sloping-throatplate boilers and housing the regulator within, and for altering many of the early domeless boilers in similar fashion.

Before the beginning of World War II desultory experiments with twin exhausts had been made on a selection of LMSR locomotives, but apart from the double-exhaust that became standard on the Duchess Pacifics none was of long duration. Jubilee No. 5684 carried a Kylchap double exhaust from the end of 1937 to the autumn of 1938. It ran freely, and in normal service on the Euston-Birmingham line was recorded as developing 1000dbhp and around 1400rhp at 60mph without forcing. In 1940 Nos. 5553 and 5742 were fitted with a plain twin-exhaust system; trials on No. 5553 (vertical-throatplate boiler) did not last long, but No. 5742 (sloping-throatplate boiler) ran with this equipment until November 1955, that is, until a few months before further twin-exhaust trials began at Rugby test plant.

Modifications to boiler and mechanical portion already mentioned were generally applied to the whole class, but some others were not so fitted, either because they were small-scale experiments or because gradual conversion was scheduled and then countermanded before all 191 locomotives had been altered. In the former category No. 5606 was fitted pre-war with TAB (Trofinoff Auto-Bypass) piston valves, while in 1938-39 No. 5654 ran with the American Ashcroft cut-off selector (sometimes called a pilot valve in England), the real purpose of

which was to help the driver to get maximum possible acceleration up to speed without slipping, but which on No. 5654 seems to have been diverted to try and lower coal consumption.

Fitting of some Jubilees (including Nos. 5621, 5651 and 5690) with BTH speedometers was begun in 1938, though No. 5660 got Stone-Deuta equipment. From May 1940 all these were removed because of war conditions, and not until early BR days were any Jubilees re-equipped, when Nos. 45578, 45616 and 45680 got modified BTH apparatus with chain drive.

Ash ejectors were put on Nos. 5671, 5698, 5702 and 5708 and possibly a few others during 1943-45. These had a small cylinder secured to the left-hand side of the smokebox from which several small pipes emerged and entered the smokebox lower down. No further application of this fitting was made, and it seems to have been removed after a few years. From 1942 the intermediate back-facing damper was welded shut, and then the whole ashpan was improved; from 1951 the discharge of the continuous blowdown was brought to the ashpan instead of being conducted to the tender.

Under the general evaluation of LMSR frames given by E. S. Cox in *Locomotive Frames* (Institution of Locomotive Engineers, 1948) Class 5XP frames were regarded as good in relation to cracks, but they were not free from that defect, and as early as 1939 a decision was made to replace the small cast-steel stretchers at the coupled horns by simpler mild steel stays. In

Part of the frame strengthening plate round the driving horns can be seen in this view of the remains of *Windward Islands* being lifted into trucks for removal to Crewe after the Harrow collision in October 1952.

1945 authorisation was given to rivet strengthening plates round the centre coupled horn gaps 'to alleviate the considerable expenditure in maintenance due to cracks developing', but this reason was applicable more to the Class 5s, to which similar plates had been fitted to some engines from authorisation given in 1939. Not all Jubilees had received these plates when in 1951 work was stopped and a more comprehensive series of frame and running-gear improvements begun. Most of these alterations were directed to the Class 5s and are explained in more detail in the fourth chapter of this book. The Jubilees were scheduled to get the Horwich type of link-and-pin cross-stay at the horns and new axlebox guides with manganese-steel liners, but comparatively few had been so treated when the programme was discontinued at the end of 1958. Yet a further improvement to the ashpan also was on the list in the 1950s.

At an earlier date the Jubilees had shared in the general programme of fitting Stanier mainline engines with stronger bogie side-control springs (authorised in October 1945 and begun in 1946), and replacing the 12-plate coupled box springs with a more flexible type having sixteen thinner plates (from 1938).

By 1940 the 191 Jubilees at work were fulfilling Stanier's criteria for a good modern steam locomotive, that is they were capable of: eight to ten hours' continuous work without recoaling; eight successive days at work without shed examination or attention, then eighteen to twenty-four hours on shed for boiler washout, standard examination and minor repairs; 40,000 miles between piston and valve examinations in shed; around 70,000 miles between wheel and axlebox attention and light repairs; and 150,000 miles or more before boiler repairs and general overhaul, when the locomotive would be in shops fifteen to twenty days.

During early BR years the Jubilees, according to R. C. Bond in *Organisation of Locomotive Repairs* (Institution of Locomotive Engineers, 1953), were averaging 67,000 miles between a major repair and the next ensuing intermediate; the breakdown showed that 6 per cent of the class went over 90,000 miles, 18 per cent covered 80,000 to 90,000, 21 per cent went 70,000 to 80,000, 20 per cent did 60,000 to 70,000, 18 per cent ran 50,000 to 60,000, 12 per cent went 40,000 to 50,000, 3 per cent went 30,000 to 40,000, and 2 per cent covered less than 30,000 miles.

TABLE VI JUBILEE PERFORMANCE IN BR DAYS (1)

| Year | L M Region | | Scottish Region | |
	Mileage	Availability %	Mileage	Availability %
1950	51,971	76	44,476	68
1951	50,691	76	44,566	70
1952	52,307	74	44,592	72
1953	53,714	75	50,400	73
1954	54,291	75	51,396	78
1955	51,833	71	47,125	73
1956	54,004	72	50,029	77
1957	51,945	73	48,923	75
1958	49,709	74	38,102	67
1959	48,967	(2)	38,190	(2)
1960	44,468	(2)	40,312	(2)
1961	32,542	(2)	30,308	(2)

(1) Mileage given is average/loco/year.
(2) Availability recording discontinued.

Jubilee annual performance through a dozen years of BR is given in Table VI. Probably the greater annual mileage got out of the LMR engines was due to the longer through runs practicable on that region. Availability figures were quite comparable with those of other mainline power, and were on the BR basis of 313 days a year.

In September/October 1934 several dynamometer-car comparative runs were made with engines of the two 5XP classes (Patriots and Jubilees), principally with Nos. 5551 and 5556 respectively, on the 12.25pm Wolverhampton-Euston and 4.35pm Euston-Wolverhampton trains, which had a two-hour schedule between Euston and Birmingham with two intermediate stops. The Patriots had a 24-element superheater parallel boiler and the Jubilees a 14-element taper boiler. There was 100°F difference in final steam temperature between the two. There was little to choose in the speeds and times of the two, and with 340 to 410 tons trailing both exerted 1450 to 1640 rail hp ascending both sides of Tring at 60-66mph. Similar runs were made in February/March 1937 with Jubilee No. 5707 (with 24-element superheater and sloping-throatplate firebox) and some Patriots on the 8.40am Birmingham-Euston and 5.50pm Euston-Birmingham expresses; in November of the same year the Kylchap Jubilee No. 5684 ran trials on the same services against Patriot No. 5533.

In April 1937 No. 5614 *Leeward Islands* ran a couple of days of dynamometer-car trials between St. Pancras and Leeds with a 302-ton nine-car formation, making one return trip via Leicester and one via Nottingham on successive

Above: Sloping-throatplate engine No. 45712 accelerates a Saturday Morecambe-Glasgow train from a slack through Tebay station before the four-mile 1 in 75 ascent to Shap summit, July 1961. *(Derek Cross)*

Below: Leeds-based NBL-built Jubilee with dome, but still carrying in BR days the original twin smokebox saddles, hauling a fast freight up the south side of Shap, banked in rear by a tank engine. *(Eric Treacy)*

**TABLE VII BRISTOL—GLASGOW TEST RESULTS; JUBILEE LOCOMOTIVE No 5660 Rooke;
302 tons trailing**

Date Trip Distance		12/10/1937 Bristol—Leeds 205.9	13/10/1937 Leeds—Glasgow 228.5	14/10/1937 Glasgow—Leeds 228.5	15/10/1937 Leeds—Bristol 205.9
	miles				
Average running speed	mph	55.4	56.3	56.8	55.3
Coal cons (running)	lb/mile	53.7	42.7	43.6	51.1
Coal consumption	lb/dbhphr	4.16	3.93	3.87	3.81
Coal consumption	lb/sfg/hr	96.4	77.7	80.2	91.3
Water cons (running)	gal/mile	33.7	29.7	28.6	35.0
Water consumption	lb/dhphr	26.1	27.3	25.5	26.2
Evaporation	lbs water /lb coal	6.26	6.94	6.58	6.86

days. Some of the times attained were: Leicester-London, 99 miles in 92.5 minutes, or 64.1mph average; London-Nottingham, 123.5 miles in 117.2 minutes, or 63.1mph average; Leicester-Leeds, 97 miles in 103 minutes, or 56.5mph average; Sheffield-Leeds, 39.5 miles in 43 minutes, or 55mph average; Nottingham-London, 123.5 miles in 114.8 minutes, or 64.3mph average. The London-Nottingham runs were made in times 12 to 14 minutes less than the fastest normal schedules of the day, and the Leicester-London run was 12½ minutes quicker than the best of 105 minutes for a regular run. Outputs recorded included 1185dbhp at 46-47mph up 1 in 100 and 1170dbhp at 71mph up 1 in 330; the latter would be equal to over 1700ihp. Throughout its life *Leeward Islands* was known as a fast and free runner.

These brief tests were preparatory to sanction being given to substantial Midland Division accelerations in the winter 1937/38 timetables. For the new timings between London, Leeds and Carlisle, and for some of the London-Derby and Leeds-Bristol trains, fifty-one Jubilees were allocated: nineteen to Kentish Town, seven to Derby, three to Sheffield, five to Nottingham, and seventeen to Leeds (Holbeck). They were able to meet the new schedules day after day. With loads of 225 to 300 tons top speeds of 90-93mph (6.35 revs/sec) were known, and 70-72mph sustained up 1 in 200 with 235 tons. No. 5734 was noted doing the Leicester-London run in just under 91 minutes with 290 tons trailing.

October 1937 saw even more striking dynamometer-car trials than those of April, with No. 5660 *Rooke,* a Derby-built 24-element superheater vertical-throatplate engine. With the same train formation as in April, *Rooke* ran in four successive days: Bristol-Leeds (205.9 miles), Leeds-Glasgow via the MR-GSWR route (228.5 miles), Glasgow-Leeds (228.5 miles), and Leeds-Bristol (205.9 miles), or 869 miles total.

On these tests *Rooke* had a 3500-gallon new-style tender, and Grimesthorpe (Yorks) coal of about 14,500 BThU/lb was fired. A Bristol crew ran the southern section in each direction and a Holbeck crew the northern section. In general, the throttle was wide open and the cut-off was adjusted to suit the conditions. The vertical-throatplate boiler now showed no signs of restricted performance, and the pressure could be kept to 220-225lb/sq in on the hardest sections, even after a hundred miles of operation beforehand, but of course with the skilled firing of those days and the best locomotive coal obtainable.

Relevant consumption and firing rates are given in Table VII, and they were obtained not from four long non-stop runs but from trips in which all regular-train stops were made, *viz* Gloucester, Cheltenham, Bromsgrove (for attachment of two 0-6-0T bankers up Lickey), Birmingham, Derby, Sheffield, Leeds, Carlisle, Annan, Dumfries and Kilmarnock. Southbound the Bromsgrove stop was replaced by the momentary brake-check stop at Blackwell, prior to descending Lickey.

The route was more steeply-graded than in the April tests, and sustained outputs uphill could be measured reliably, especially up the 13.9 miles from Settle Junction to Blea Moor, almost entirely at 1 in 100, up which average speed was 51.1mph (bank begun at 63mph), average dbhp 1129, and maximum dbhp 1240, both at 35 per cent cut-off. Maximum ihp was calculated at 1844. Accelerating up the three miles of 1 in 100 from Heeley to Dore & Totley on the fourth day, average dbhp was 1185 and the maximum 1240; over this stretch cut-off was reduced gradually from 45 to 35 per cent, and average speed was 42.5mph, though as *Rooke* was accelerating all the time the speed at the top was 46.5mph. Fast accelerations were a feature of the whole four days.

Southbound from Carlisle the train was

worked up a vertical distance of 1150ft to Ais Gill summit in 48.4 miles in a time of 48min 36sec start-to-pass, or 60mph. Up the last three miles of 1 in 100 to Ais Gill with full throttle and 35 to 40 per cent cut-off the minimum speed was 46.5mph, dbhp averaged above 1050 with a maximum of 1113, and maximum ihp was estimated at 1773.

A special trip was run by a Jubilee for the Institution of Locomotive Engineers from Manchester to Derby on 13 May 1949 with dynamometer car, two mobile test units and three coaches attached, equal to a trailing load of 270 tons. Continuous outputs up to 1050dbhp at 32mph up 1 in 90 were reached with 45 per cent cut-off and full throttle, and short-time outputs up to 1430dbhp at 50mph up 1 in 105 were attained.

All these were actual drawbar readings. On normal service runs equivalent dbhps (edbhp) of 1400 to 1500 and even more were achieved on numerous occasions, particularly on ascents to Blea Moor and Ais Gill and up the 1 in 200 between Bedford and Leagrave, and both before and after World War II. At a much later date, 13 March 1955, dynamometer-car trials were made up the 1 in 37 of Lickey with No. 45554 hauling 252 tons without banking assistance. Starts were made with the train wholly on the grade, though with some difficulty, and in one case without success, the engine and train having to coast back down to Bromsgrove. A week previously, Class 5 No. 44776 was similarly tested with 220 tons trailing.

In 1938 Stanier gave curves of ihp and dbhp for the Jubilees as shown in Fig. 10, but he emphasised that these were based on average economical running conditions, kept to around 1300ihp maximum, and not on top outputs obtainable over short times. By these, a Jubilee could be rated to take 500 tons along the straight level at 60mph. Above the Stanier curves in Fig. 10 have been added curves of some of the higher outputs recorded on dynamometer-car tests and in normal service, the latter often when time was being made up. Some of these figures were obtained well on in BR days, when the Jubilees were worked (and could take it) just as hard as they ever were in the first five or six years of their lives. Stanier reckoned in 1938 that with a firing rate of 100lb/sfg/hr a Jubilee could peak 1800ihp, and there were occasions in service when that power must have been just attained.

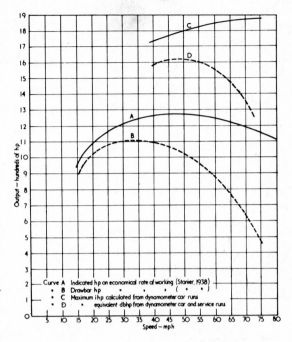

Fig 10 Curves of Jubilee indicated and drawbar horsepowers.

As they were delivered, the first one or two Jubilees were put on the Euston-Birmingham services; and then the first five spent a short time at Preston depot working the Lakes Express, Fylde Coast Express and similar trains. On such duties, with 250/275-ton formations along the Western Division main line, the fire could go untouched for thirty miles and more. Most succeeding deliveries before the end of 1934 went to the Midland Division for the London-Leeds and Leeds-Bristol routes. Though successful on the western route, the few Bristol-based engines were removed temporarily because of more urgent needs on the London-Leeds line and on the Western Division, as the hardest Bristol turns could be diagrammed for engines shedded at Leeds.

Early duties on the Western Division additional to the Birmingham services included the Liverpool and Manchester to Glasgow and Edinburgh trains, on which through runs up to 230 miles were made, and rail horsepowers (rhp) of 1300 to 1600 were attained occasionally uphill. Jubilees were not often seen on the Holyhead line in pre-war years, but from time to time worked Lancashire-West of England trains to Shrewsbury and beyond. They also put up regular lively performances on the Liverpool-

Cold-water washout through reducing valve at ground hydrant and non-leak helix connections below the cab footsteps. By this time the vertical-throatplate boiler of *Sandwich* had been provided with a dome, the original gravity sanding had been replaced by steam, the vacuum pump had been removed, and the de-sanders discarded. *(J. B. Radford collection)*

Manchester line with 200/275-ton trains, and often reached 1400-1500rhp for short times accelerating up slight grades.

When the Euston-Birmingham services were for the first time in history cut below a two-hour schedule, as from 30 September 1935, the Jubilees were put on to handle them, and the first down train was hauled by the Camden-based *Silver Jubilee* itself with a load of 350 tons. The first up journey was made by No. 5557 with 285 tons trailing, and *Silver Jubilee* returned with the first up evening train to the new timing. There was an intermediate stop at Willesden in each direction, which meant 62mph start-to-stop between that station and Birmingham. In 1939 the fourteen Patriots based on Aston and Bushbury sheds for working the Wolverhampton-Birmingham-Euston express services were replaced by fourteen Jubilees, all of the sloping-throatplate variety and all in the number range 5719-42.

On certain turns, Western Division Jubilees arriving at Glasgow filled in some of their lie-by time on passenger trains to Largs, and later in the 1930s Polmadie-based engines were used on fast trains to Ayr over the ex-GSWR line, sometimes from 1939 going on to Stranraer. On fast schedules to Ayr they were noted as able to develop over 900dbhp at 70mph. Early in the war years they took over all the Glasgow-Stranraer trains from the Class 5 4-6-0s.

In the summer of 1938 Western Division Jubilees often hauled the up Edinburgh-Aberdeen portion of the Royal Scot through from Carlisle to Euston, probably the longest through runs they ever made, and certainly the longest non-stop run, and they were known to make the 299 miles in about 280 minutes net (ie after allowance for signal checks) with 285 tons, exerting 1375-1400rhp and more at 50mph on uphill stretches.

The ex-Caledonian section also had eight to ten shedded at Balornock (St. Rollox) in the mid-1930s, such as Nos. 5571, 5577-8, 5583-4 and 5644-5, most of which had been built by NBL. These operated Glasgow-Perth-Aberdeen services, but while equipped with 14-element superheaters were reckoned by the Scots to be no better than the ex-Caledonian 4-6-0s and Midland compounds; when altered to 24-

element superheaters the very fast intermediate times they gave on the Aberdeen-Perth section were a surprise to Scottish enginemen. Scottish-based engines, because of the good water, could go 2,000 miles and more between washouts, whereas in England not more than 1,800 miles and often 15 to 20 per cent less could be run before washing-out. At this period practically all LMSR wash-out facilities were with cold water.

After a large-scale transfer from the Western Division early in 1935, most of the Jubilees then in traffic were concentrated on the Midland Division, and by the summer of that year practically every one of the thirty daily runs timed at over 60mph on that division was performed regularly by one or other of the class, and they were capable of taking 340 tons from London to Leicester in ninety-seven minutes; even the 14-element superheater engines could do this. They had some power margin with 300-ton loads on these schedules, but traffic delays on ex-MR lines were numerous in 1935-38 and led to many out-of-course decelerations and re-accelerations.

Delivery of the last seventy-eight Jubilees was mainly to the Western and Central Divisions, and from then onwards the class could be found on all major LMSR routes from London and Bristol in the south to Aberdeen in the north, to Holyhead and Hereford in the west, and to York in the east. Because of bridge strength, not until July 1938 were the Jubilees permitted over the Peak Forest line between Derby and Manchester, and they then took over most of the express working and were allowed 275 tons unpiloted over the 1 in 90 against the 255 tons of the Class 5s.

An early special working was that of No. 5552 *Silver Jubilee* from St. Pancras to Kettering with the honeymoon train of the Duke and Duchess of Gloucester on 6 November 1935. Nos. 5741 and 5742 double-headed in each direction between London and Huyton the Royal train for the Grand National week in April 1937; No. 5587 and another double-headed the Royal train from Crewe to Stranraer on 27 July 1937 for the visit of King George VI and Queen Elizabeth to Belfast, while Nos. 5670 and 5678 double-headed the Royal train between Crewe and Carlisle on 1 July 1938 en route to the funeral of the Countess of Strathmore at Glamis. No. 5593 hauled Mr Winston Churchill's war-time special from Liverpool to Euston on his return from the USA in 1942, and a further recorded Royal

working was in May 1948 when No. M5606 took a train from London to Birmingham.

The Jubilees got through the war years handling heavy loads, up to thirteen coaches on the Manchester-Derby line in place of the pre-war 'statutory' nine, and under the constantly deteriorating standards of handling and maintenance then prevalent, which in later years were never wholly overcome. For the remainder of its corporate existence the LMSR carried out no further modifications to the class, and did not even attempt to fit self-cleaning smokeboxes, commonly applied to new engines from 1945.

Through 1945-48 many Jubilees were being worked harder than in pre-war years, for while speeds were not so high, numerous trains of 375 to 450 tons were being handled unpiloted on the Western and Midland Divisions, even over Ais Gill in each direction, and they had to accelerate from more numerous stops. Long continuous runs remained, such as Leeds-Glasgow (228 miles) and Bristol-York (232 miles), though coal quality was poor and firing standards often mediocre.

TABLE VIII JUBILEE DISTRIBUTION 1937–58

Year	Western Division	Midland Division	Central Division	Northern Division
1937	101	44	27	19
1948	70	68	24	29
1958 (1)	74	66	21	29

(1) 1958 figures adjusted to correspond to LMS divisions, not BR Regions.

Distribution also was rather different. Table VIII shows the pre-war, post-war and **BR** allocations. The 1958 figures relate to former LMSR divisions and not regional ownership; that year's total also reflects the withdrawal some years previously of No. 45637. BR depots normally having the largest allocations were Willesden, Crewe North, Preston, Upperby, Kentish Town, Leeds (Holbeck), Newton Heath and Kingmoor, but towards the end of steam Burton suddenly found itself possessed of no fewer than eighteen in December 1961, while around 1960-61 Glasgow Corkerhill had eleven.

A gradual extension of duties followed nationalisation, the most notable and long-standing being beyond Leeds and York to Newcastle. Elsewhere in the north-east Jubilees penetrated on holiday trains to Saltburn, Bridlington, Scarborough, Hull and Skegness; and in 1959-60 they also took turns on the Sutton Coldfield-Stirling car-sleeper. Trips well

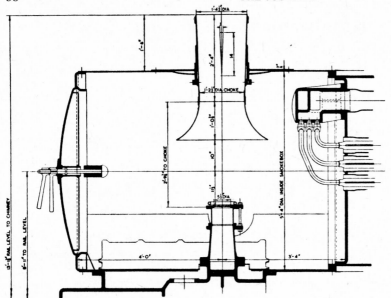

to the south also came in the last decade of steam, but were not welcome on the restricted Central Section of the Southern Region, where in 1961 No. 45650 reached Brighton on an excursion and was prohibited from working back on a train. In 1962 No. 45672 reached Newhaven on a train, but after failing at Lewes on the return was held there, and the next day No. 45617 was similarly held at Newhaven. Both were allowed home light after about a fortnight while routes were checked, with a limit of 25mph over the SR.

After the formation of BR the overall performance of the Jubilees and other classes was closely examined, but no Jubilee was engaged in the 1948 Interchange Trials, as no 5XP-class tests were made. The Jubilees remained in the 5XP classification until the BR revision scheme of January 1951, when they became 6P, which lasted until November 1955 when a final official classification of 6P5F was given; this was never put on the cab, which continued to bear simply *6P*. The BR system for passenger engines was based on a combination of tractive effort and boiler power, whereas the LMSR system had been grounded on tractive effort only.

Opening of the Rugby stationary test plant in

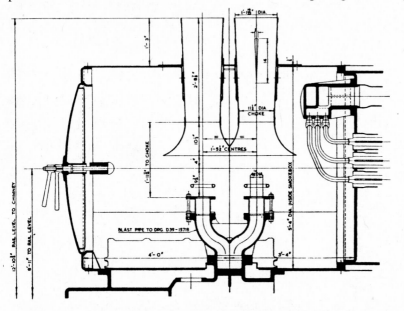

October 1948 gave possibilities of wider examinations, but not until 1956 did one of the Jubilees, No. 45722 *Defence*, get there with a view to improving its steaming power, especially with coal not of the best. With the then normal best coal maximum steam generation in the pre-war sloping-throatplate 3A boiler was found to be under 21,000 lb/hr with a back pressure of 6.8 lb/sq in; with second-class coal evaporation was not above 18,000 lb/hr. In efforts to raise the capacity to 25,000 lb/hr the chimney was first increased in diameter, and the standard taper inside from the choke upwards was altered from 1 in 7 to 1 in 14. Also the tapered blastpipe was changed by replacing the top portion with a parallel section of 5½in orifice diameter

contrasted with the 5⅛in to 4¾in diameters of the old taper pipes. This new arrangement (Fig 11) gave almost 20 per cent increase in evaporative power, but with an increase of 18 per cent in back pressure to 8.1 lb/sq in.

Experiments then were made with a double blastpipe of the parallel type noted above, each nozzle being 4⅛in diameter, surmounted by twin chimneys with 11¼in diameter chokes. This layout (Fig 12) produced a maximum evaporation above 25,000 lb/hr with the reduced back pressure of only 5.7 lb/sq in, i.e. a gain at both ends of the scale. At lower rates of working the twin exhaust produced 20,700 lb/hr of steam with a back pressure of only 3.8 lb/sq in.

Put another way, the pre-war 3A boiler-

No. 5609 outside Derby works in May 1948 after being involved in an accident at Rotherham. Still with LMS insignia. One of the few Jubilees with double-row nameplates. *(H. C. Casserley)*

smokebox-blastpipe ensemble at 21,000 lb/hr evaporation required 3,324 lb/hr of coal, equal to a firing rate of 107 lb/sfg/hr, and produced 12.67 lb steam/hr/sq ft of evaporative surface. With the new twin-exhaust layout and 25,000 lb/hr evaporation the respective figures were 4,435, 143 and 15.2. With a low grade of coal of 11,270 B.Th.U/lb calorific value the twin-exhaust system gave a maximum evaporation of 21,750 lb/hr and respective values of 4,220, 136 and 13.26.

Despite these betterments the test double-exhaust was removed from No. 45722 in 1957 and only one Jubilee, No. 45596, was equipped subsequently with a twin exhaust having 4⅜in diameter nozzles, probably because by the time the tests were finished in the spring of 1957 the period of steam was running out and the foreseeable duties for the Jubilees were thought not likely to require more than 20,000 lb/hr of steam. Single-exhaust modifications on the lines of the Rugby intermediate stage were made to Nos. 45601/10/22/28/72/88 and 47533/38. This is more surprising in that the long-standing plain double exhaust on No. 5742 had given noticeably good results, and that engine could work the 330/350-ton Birmingham two-hour trains on 40-42 lb coal/mile and 32-33 gallons water/mile.

Yet some of the hardest work in Jubilee life came shortly after the Rugby trials, with the big acceleration of Midland main-line services in the summer of 1957. This brought schedules equal to 1938 standards with loads averaging 6 to 8 per cent more, and worked by the same power except that power was now nineteen years older and had experienced years of handling, maintenance and fuel inferior to those of 1938.

The XL limit for the Jubilees on these trains was 300 tons; but though the engines were known to make times of 93-94 minutes Leicester to London with 325-350 tons, much piloting was needed to maintain punctuality with varying weather and coal, and the frequent traffic delays—piloting that might have been avoided if the experimental twin exhaust had been fitted more widely. Coincidentally with these Midland accelerations the Jubilees were doing equally good work on the Euston-Birmingham trains, with loads up to the XL limit of 350 tons and on Rugby-Euston schedules of 79 minutes for 82.6 miles.

With the mass introduction of diesels in the early 1960s the Jubilees were mainly demoted to a mixed bag of secondary trains, though always capable of being put on to a higher-class duty in case of a diesel or other steam failure. Several in their last two or three years put in much time on fitted freights over Midland lines. Others drifted into Eastern and Western Region care, working on the ex-Great Central route from Neasden, Annesley and Darnall depots, and on ex-GWR and joint lines out of Chester, and several were finally condemned from the stock of those regions. The ER/NER gave the allocated engines the RA8 route availability code.

Few additions or alterations were made by BR. Not until 1959-60 was a beginning made with fitting aws apparatus and comparatively few engines were so equipped, but all remaining in 1965-67 had been furnished. They could be distinguished by the small cylindrical vacuum reservoir on the right-hand side and a similar but smaller timing reservoir on the left-hand side, each on the running plate just in front of the cab, and by the small vacuum pipe clipped to the left-hand running angle leading to the aws mechanism in front of the bogie, protected from coupling swing by a plate. Beginning with No. 45567 in January 1961, a few engines were given Stone-Deuta speedometers driven off the left-hand trailing crankpin. From 1962 the Jubilees had the red flash signs on the firebox, below the top feed, and on the frame front end as a reminder of the presence of overhead wires.

The Jubilees were a lucky class in being involved in few serious accidents in a gross life around 5,750 locomotive-years. No. 45637 *Windward Islands* was piloting the northbound express in the Harrow disaster on 8 October 1952, and along with its train engine, the rebuilt Pacific No. 46202 *Princess Anne,* was so badly damaged that it was withdrawn for scrap in the December. This made the Jubilee total 188, plus the two big-boiler rebuilds, for the next eight years until regular withdrawal began with No. 45609 in 1960 and three more engines in 1961.

Withdrawal dates of all are given in Table IX. The last few in traffic worked from Leeds (Holbeck) during 1967, and for some weeks over the route thence to Carlisle provided the last

chance of travelling behind express steam locomotives in normal service. Last in traffic were Nos. 45562, 45593 and 45697, which all worked to October/November 1967, the 'official' last being No. 45562. Nos. 45589 and 45697 were the last to be given general overhauls, and came out of Crewe in good order as late as April-June 1965, repainted BR green unlined

Three Jubilees are preserved, all in working order. They are Nos. 45593 *Kolhapur* at the Birmingham Railway Museum, Tyseley (purchased in January 1968 by 7029 Clun Castle Ltd); 45596 *Bahamas*, at Dinting (finally purchased in August 1967 for around £3000 by the Bahamas Locomotive Society (Stockport)); and 45690, also at Dinting and the property of the same group. *Bahamas* ran with its double chimney from May 1961 until withdrawal in June 1966, and after being stored in Edgeley (Stockport) depot was sent to the Hunslet Engine Company's works for general overhaul. By that time the original nameplates had disappeared, and new ones with the Bahamas crest above were made. The engine emerged from Hunslet, still with double chimney and repainted, in March 1968, with new oval works and number plates bearing 'No. 5596 Rebuilt 1968'.

TABLE IX JUBILEE CLASS 4–6–0 LOCOMOTIVES, LMSR/BR

No	Name(s)	Date into traffic	1st domed boiler	Date BR No	Withdrawn	Notes
5552		5/34				(1)
5552	Silver Jubilee	ex 5642 in 4/35	9/40	9/51	9/64	(5)
5553	Canada	6/34	2/37	6/49	11/64	(7)
5554	Ontario	6/34	6/36	11/48	11/64	
5555	Quebec	6/34	10/38	4/48	8/63	(5)
5556	Nova Scotia	6/34	2/37	3/49	9/64	(5)
5557	New Brunswick	6/34	2/37	5/48	9/64	
5558	Manitoba	7/34	11/37	9/48	8/64	
5559	British Columbia	7/34	10/37	11/48	10/62	
5560	Prince Edward Island	7/34	6/37	8/48	11/63	
5561	Saskatchewan	7/34	2/38	5/48	9/64	
5562	Alberta	8/34	6/37	10/48	11/67	(5)
5563	Australia	8/34	1/39	6/49	11/65	
5564	New South Wales	8/34	7/37	4/49	7/64	
5565	Victoria	8/34	6/37	5/48	1/67	
5566	Queensland	8/34	3/37	6/48	11/62	
5567	South Australia	8/34	4/37	11/48	1/65	(2)
5568	Western Australia	8/34	6/37	10/48	4/64	
5569	Tasmania	8/34	6/37	12/48	4/64	
5570	New Zealand	8/34	8/37	6/48	12/62	
5571	South Africa	9/34	5/38	10/48	5/64	
5572	Irish Free State; Eire 9/38	9/34	5/37	8/48	1/64	
5573	Newfoundland	9/34	3/38	9/48	9/65	
5574	India	9/34	11/37	6/49	3/66	
5575	Madras	9/34	12/37	8/48	6/63	(5)
5576	Bombay	9/34	6/41	6/48	12/62	(5)

No	Name(s)	Date into traffic	1st domed boiler	Date BR No	Withdrawn	Notes
5577	Bengal	9/34	7/39	4/48	9/64	(5)
5578	United Provinces	9/34	4/38	12/48	5/64	(5)
5579	Punjab	10/34	5/38	8/48	8/64	(5)
5580	Burma	10/34	6/37	5/49	12/64	(5)
5581	Bihar and Orissa	10/34	4/43	4/48	8/66	(5)
5582	Central Provinces	11/34	11/37	2/49	12/62	
5583	Assam	11/34	1/38	10/48	10/64	
5584	North West Frontier	12/34	8/38	3/48	9/64	
5585	Hyderabad	12/34	6/37	5/48	5/64	
5586	Mysore	12/34	2/37	6/48	1/65	(5)
5587	Baroda	12/34	3/37	6/48	12/62	
5588	Kashmir	12/34	6/37	6/49	4/65	
5589	Gwalior	12/34	10/37	6/48	3/65	
5590	Travancore	12/34	4/37	9/48	12/65	(2)
5591	Udaipur	12/34	6/38	9/48	10/63	(5)
5592	Indore	12/34	5/37	6/48	9/64	(5)
5593	Kolhapur	12/34	4/37	12/48	10/67	(11)
5594	Bhopal	1/35	1/38	2/49	12/62	
5595	Southern Rhodesia	1/35	3/37	9/49	1/65	
5596	Bahamas	1/35	11/37	5/48	7/66	(7)(11)
5597	Barbados	1/35	2/38	8/48	1/65	
5598	Basutoland	2/35	6/37	4/48	10/64	
5599	Bechuanaland	1/35	8/37	8/48	8/64	
5600	Bermuda	2/35	2/38	7/48	12/65	(5)
5601	British Guiana	4/35	9/37	4/49	9/64	(5)(8)
5602	British Honduras	4/35	4/37	8/49	3/65	
5603	Solomon Islands	3/35	10/37	3/49	12/62	
5604	Ceylon	3/35	7/37	4/48	7/65	
5605	Cyprus	4/35	4/38	7/48	2/64	
5606	Falkland Islands	4/35	2/38	5/49	6/64	(8)(9)
5607	Fiji	6/34	6/36	5/48	11/62	(3)(5)
5608	Gibraltar	7/34	4/37	9/48	9/65	(2)
5609	Gilbert and Ellice Islands	7/34	9/38	8/48	9/60	
5610	Gold Coast; Ghana 12/58	7/34	2/37	6/49	1/64	(4)(8)
5611	Hong Kong	7/34	8/38	11/48	9/64	
5612	Jamaica	8/34	4/37	12/48	3/64	
5613	Kenya	8/34	11/38	8/48	9/64	
5614	Leeward Islands	8/34	12/36	4/48	1/64	
5615	Malay States	8/34	2/37	4/48	12/62	(5)
5616	Malta; Malta G.C. 11/43	8/34	7/36	9/48	1/61	(3)
5617	Mauritius	9/34	12/37	6/48	11/64	
5618	New Hebrides	10/34	4/37	5/48	2/64	(5)
5619	Nigeria	10/34	3/37	6/48	8/61	
5620	North Borneo	10/34	3/37	9/48	9/64	
5621	Northern Rhodesia	10/34	6/37	10/48	12/62	(2)
5622	Nyasaland	10/34	7/36	6/48	9/64	(3)(8)
5623	Palestine	10/34	8/39	6/48	7/64	
5624	St Helena	10/34	12/38	9/48	11/63	
5625	Sarawak	10/34	1/39	10/49	9/63	
5626	Seychelles	11/34	2/37	3/49	10/65	
5627	Sierra Leone	11/34	10/38	10/48	9/66	
5628	Somaliland	11/34	2/37	12/48	12/62	(8)
5629	Straits Settlements	11/34	4/39	11/48	4/65	
5630	Swaziland	11/34	11/38	6/48	11/61	
5631	Tanganyika	11/34	12/38	11/48	8/64	
5632	Tonga	11/34	8/38	5/49	10/65	
5633	Trans-Jordan; Aden 9/46	11/34	10/39	12/48	10/65	
5634	Trinidad	11/34	4/39	12/49	5/63	
5635	Tobago	11/34	3/39	5/49	9/64	
5636	Uganda	12/34	3/37	2/49	12/62	(5)
5637	Windward Islands	12/34	10/38	9/48	12/52	
5638	Zanzibar	12/34	11/36	6/48	3/64	
5639	Raleigh	12/34	3/37	7/48	9/63	(2)
5640	Frobisher	12/34	8/36	5/48	3/64	(2)
5641	Sandwich	12/34	4/37	9/48	9/64	
5642		12/34				(1)
5642	Boscawen	ex 5552 in 4/35	12/39	5/48	1/65	
5643	Rodney	12/34	6/44	9/48	1/66	(5)
5644	Howe	12/34	10/38	11/48	11/63	(5)
5645	Collingwood	12/34	9/37	6/48	10/63	(5)

No	Name(s)	Date into traffic	1st domed boiler	Date BR No	Withdrawn	Notes
5646	Napier	12/34	3/38	12/48	12/63	(5)
5647	Sturdee	1/35	1/38	8/49	4/67	
5648	Wemyss	1/35	12/37	6/48	2/63	(5)
5649	Hawkins	1/35	4/37	8/48	10/63	
5650	Blake	1/35	1/37	2/49	1/63	
5651	Shovell	1/35	10/37	6/49	11/62	(5)
5652	Hawke	1/35	5/37	10/48	1/65	
5653	Barham	1/35	1/38	10/48	3/65	(5)
5654	Hood	2/35	5/37	1/49	6/66	
5655	Keith	12/34	5/37	2/49	4/65	
5656	Cochrane	12/34	3/37	4/48	12/62	
5657	Tyrwhitt	12/34	4/37	8/48	9/64	(2)
5658	Keyes	12/34	6/37	5/49	9/65	
5659	Drake	12/34	5/37	8/48	5/63	
5660	Rooke	12/34	7/37	5/48	6/66	
5661	Vernon	12/34	1/38	8/49	5/65	
5662	Kempenfelt	12/34	7/38	8/48	11/62	
5663	Jervis	1/35	7/38	8/48	10/64	
5664	Nelson	1/35	4/37	11/48	5/65	
5665	Lord Rutherford of Nelson	11/35	New	3/49	12/62	
5666	Cornwallis	11/35	New	12/48	4/65	
5667	Jellicoe	11/35	New	4/49	1/65	
5668	Madden	12/35	New	4/49	12/63	
5669	Fisher	12/35	New	8/48	5/63	
5670	Howard of Effingham	12/35	New	3/49	10/64	
5671	Prince Rupert	12/35	New	4/49	11/63	
5672	Anson	12/35	New	8/48	11/64	(8)
5673	Keppel	12/35	New	4/48	12/62	
5674	Duncan	12/35	New	6/48	10/64	
5675	Hardy	12/35	New	9/48	6/67	
5676	Codrington	12/35	New	9/48	9/64	
5677	Beatty	12/35	New	8/49	12/62	(6)
5678	De Robeck	12/35	New	2/49	12/62	
5679	Armada	12/35	New	8/48	12/62	
5680	Camperdown	12/35	New	9/48	1/63	
5681	Aboukir	12/35	New	10/49	9/64	
5682	Trafalgar	1/36	New	3/49	6/64	
5683	Hogue	1/36	New	7/48	12/62	
5684	Jutland	2/36	New	10/48	12/65	(6)(7)
5685	Barfleur	2/36	New	5/48	4/64	(6)
5686	St. Vincent	2/36	New	8/49	11/62	(6)
5687	Neptune	2/36	New	10/48	12/62	
5688	Polyphemus	2/36	New	5/48	12/62	(8)
5689	Ajax	2/36	New	11/48	12/64	
5690	Leander	3/36	New	5/48	3/64	(11)
5691	Orion	3/36	New	5/49	12/62	
5692	Cyclops	3/36	New	6/48	12/62	
5693	Agamemnon	3/36	New	8/48	12/62	
5694	Bellerophon	3/36	New	4/48	1/67	
5695	Minotaur	3/36	New	10/48	1/64	
5696	Arethusa	4/36	New	10/48	7/64	(6)
5697	Achilles	4/36	New	5/48	9/67	
5698	Mars	4/36	New	9/48	10/65	
5699	Galatea	4/36	New	5/48	11/64	
5700	Britannia; Amethyst 9/51	4/36	New	12/48	7/64	
5701	Conqueror	4/36	New	5/48	2/63	
5702	Colossus	5/36	New	6/48	4/63	
5703	Thunderer	5/36	New	4/49	11/64	
5704	Leviathan	5/36	New	12/48	1/65	
5705	Seahorse	5/36	New	1/49	11/65	
5706	Express	5/36	New	8/48	9/63	
5707	Valiant	5/36	New	8/48	12/62	
5708	Resolution	6/36	New	8/48	2/64	
5709	Implacable	6/36	New	1/49	11/63	(6)
5710	Irresistible	6/36	New	2/49	6/64	
5711	Courageous	6/36	New	12/48	12/62	
5712	Victory	6/36	New	10/48	11/63	
5713	Renown	7/36	New	9/48	10/62	
5714	Revenge	7/36	New	4/49	7/63	
5715	Invincible	7/36	New	4/48	12/62	
5716	Swiftsure	7/36	New	2/49	9/64	

No	Name(s)	Date into traffic	1st domed boiler	Date BR No	Withdrawn	Notes
5717	Dauntless	7/36	New	6/49	10/63	
5718	Dreadnought	8/36	New	2/49	10/62	
5719	Glorious	8/36	New	2/49	3/63	
5720	Indomitable	8/36	New	9/48	12/62	
5721	Impregnable	8/36	New	8/48	10/65	
5722	Defence	8/36	New	7/48	11/62	
5723	Fearless	8/36	New	5/48	8/64	
5724	Warspite	9/36	New	8/48	10/62	
5725	Repulse	9/36	New	12/48	12/62	
5726	Vindictive	10/36	New	12/48	3/65	
5727	Inflexible	10/36	New	6/48	12/62	
5728	Defiance	10/36	New	10/48	10/62	
5729	Furious	10/36	New	6/48	10/62	
5730	Ocean	10/36	New	4/48	10/63	
5731	Perseverance	10/36	New	12/48	10/62	
5732	Sanspareil	10/36	New	3/49	2/64	
5733	Novelty	11/36	New	9/49	9/64	(8)
5734	Meteor	11/36	New	9/48	12/63	
5735	Comet	11/36	New	6/48	10/64	(10)
5736	Phoenix	11/36	New	9/48	9/64	(10)
5737	Atlas	11/36	New	11/48	5/64	
5738	Samson	12/36	New	6/49	12/63	(8)
5739	Ulster	12/36	New	7/48	1/67	
5740	Munster	12/36	New	6/48	10/63	
5741	Leinster	12/36	New	5/48	1/64	
5742	Connaught	12/36	New	11/48	5/65	(6)(7)

Notes

(1)   Original No 5552 re-numbered 5642 and vice versa 4/35

(2)   Fitted with sloping throatplate boiler at date shown.

(3)   Fitted with sloping throatplate boiler at date shown and then reverted to vertical throatplate boiler at following dates:—
         5607   4/38;   5616   2/38;   5622   7/38.

(4)   Fitted with sloping throatplate boiler in 9/43.

(5)   Fitted with domeless 21 element superheater boiler at the following dates:—

5642/5552 New—10/40; 4/43—5/45	5600 12/40—11/42; 7/54—6/58
5555 6/52—2/56	5601 11/53—7/56
5556 1/45—8/47	5607 12/42—10/46
5562 10/47—2/52; 2/61—11/62	5615 8/49—10/52
5575 1/50—6/60	5618 1/43—4/44
5576 12/37—5/41	5636 2/49—4/53
5577 12/51—8/53	5643 New—6/44; 3/56—8/60
5578 12/52—8/57	5644 New—10/38; 8/46—11/49
5579 4/38—5/42; 1/47—8/51	5645 New—9/37; 10/57—10/63
5580 8/41—6/42	5646 New—4/38
5581 3/39—3/43	5648 9/42—11/44
5586 2/61—1/65	5651 3/57—11/62
5591 3/60—10/63	5653 6/45—10/48
5592 6/44—3/49	

(6)   Fitted with domed 28 element superheater boiler at the following dates:—

5677 New—7/38	5696 10/38—7/41
5684 10/41—9/43	5709 11/43—4/46
5685 8/54—*	5742 9/46—10/49
5686 8/50—1/54	

     * Subsequent moves of this boiler not traced.

(7)   Double chimney fitted as follows:—

5553 —/40— ?	5684 1937—8 (Kylchap)
5596 5/61 (retained)	5742 —/40—11/55

(8)   Modified draughting in 1957.

(9)   TAB valves experimentally fitted in 1938.

(10)   Rebuilt with 2A boiler and double chimney:—
         5735   5/42;   5736   4/42.

(11)   Preserved.

CHAPTER THREE

REBUILT JUBILEES

First reconstruction or major modification of any Jubilee after boiler design had settled down was made in 1942, and it was vital to future LMSR main-line express locomotive policy and operation, though strangely, not to the Jubilee class as a whole. This work also was the first part of the last important locomotive design activity conducted under Stanier, for coincident with the completion of this work in 1942 he was seconded to government service. He remained on the LMSR books until his formal retirement from the cme's position in April 1944, but he did not return to active railway service after 1942, though he was consulted on major projects.

The particular activity now considered was the rebuilding of Nos. 5735 *Comet* and 5736 *Phoenix* with larger and higher pressure taper boilers, known as 2A, and double exhaust. From the late 1930s, partly as a result of the reconstruction of No. 6399 *Fury* into No. 6170 *British Legion*, thought had been given to increasing the boiler power of all Class 5XP engines to bring them into line with the 6P Royal Scots, for in their unrebuilt state the latter could exert economically between 40mph and 60mph ihps that were 20 per cent above Jubilee values. At first a two-cylinder rebuild was considered, so that the weight saved by the elimination of one cylinder and drive line could be put into a larger boiler with little or no increment in maximum axle load, but eventually a solution was found by which the three cylinders could be retained while putting in an enlarged boiler. Two of these new boilers were included in the 1940 programme, and the instructions for the conversions, along with the first drawings, were issued in October 1940. No. 5736 emerged in its rebuilt form in April 1942, followed in May 1942 by No. 5735. Sanctioned cost of the conversions was £3130, but the actual amount charged in the end was £3440, which would be little more than the cost of the two new boilers.

The original cylinders, motion, bogie, running gear, cab, and essentials of the frame structure were retained. The modifications put up the maximum axle load to 20.75 tons, the adhesion weight to 61.5 tons, the engine working order weight to 82 tons (see Fig 13), and the empty weight to 75.9 tons. Tractive effort was 10 per cent greater at 29,590 lb (85 per cent factor), but factor of adhesion was reduced to 4.62 from the 4.97 of the standard Jubilees. Both rebuilds according to official records retained their Stanier 4000-gallon 9-ton tenders (Nos. 9369-70), though the weights in the official diagrams for the rebuilds showed 53.65 tons gross and 26.9 tons tare, the figures for welded tenders. Engine-plus-tender wheelbase and overall length were unchanged, and engine-plus-tender working order weight totalled 135.65 tons. General dimensions are included in Table II (Chapter 2).

Phoenix as rebuilt in 1942 with double exhaust and with 2A boiler. Top feed on front ring. The speedometer was an unusual fitting for 1942 and was soon removed. The standard scroll and serif insignia reintroduced in 1938 was replaced after a few years by the sans form. *(J. B. Radford collection)*

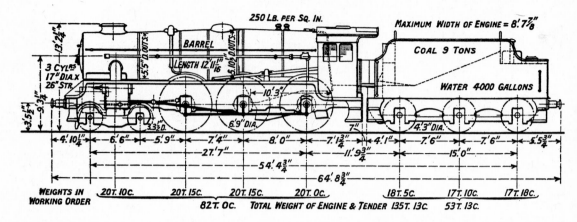

250 LB. PER SQ. IN.

Above: **Fig 13** Diagram of the two Jubilees Nos. 5735-36 rebuilt with larger type 2A boiler in 1942.

Right: Rebuilt Jubilee *Comet* on up train at Bletchley in July 1948 after being renumbered into BR stock and given sans insignia and sans numerals on smokebox plate. *(H. C. Casserley)*

The 2A was a new design of boiler with safety-valves set at 250lb/sq in, and it was the sloping-throatplate version of the similar-pressure No. 2 boiler used on No. 6170 *British Legion*. It was slightly shorter in the barrel and between tubeplates than the 3A, but was 5in greater in diameter at the front and 2¼in greater at the back. This permitted greater free area through tubes and flues (4.94sq ft against 4.55sq ft) and allowed conveniently a four-row 28-flue superheater arrangement. Tube length: bore ratio was altered some 10 per cent by a reduction in od to 1¾in. The sloping-throatplate firebox was only 3in longer than the corresponding 3A box and so grate area was a mere ¾sq ft larger; but because of the greater barrel diameter and the higher pitch of 9ft 3¼in (against 8ft 11in) the firebox volume was increased and the firebox heating surface went up 8 per cent. Dimensions of the 2A boiler are included in Table III (Chapter 2).

Top-feed clackboxes and casing were moved forward to the front ring of the barrel, which led to a rather artless arrangement of the water-delivery pipes, and one or two other crude details betokened lack of drawing-office time in the difficult early war years. The firebox had seven washout plugs per side in place of six, and the ashpan was of different shape. Because of the higher boiler pitch maximum height above rail level rose again to 13ft 2¼in at the chimney, and as the old cab was retained the firebox back came much closer to the cab roof. One or two mechanical details, such as the reach rod, were altered, and twin brake blocks were applied to each coupled wheel.

A speedometer was added to the cab equipment and was driven from the left-hand trailing crankpin. This was at a time when all speedometers had been removed from LMSR locomotives that had them at the time war began, including several Jubilees given them in 1938-39. The equipments on the rebuilds of Nos. 5735-36 seem to have been removed quickly. Some wheel rebalancing was done, and for several years, at least, the leading and trailing coupled wheels had a peculiar shape of weight, possibly due to a reduction in the amount of reciprocating balance.

As painted on conversion, Nos. 5735-36 bore the scroll and serif numerals and insignia re-introduced in 1938, but by 1947 were running with the sans type, possibly to use up sans transfers still in stock, though new cast-iron smokebox door number plates were made in the sans type.

Along with the bigger smokebox, with self-cleaning plates and twin blastpipes, the increase in evaporation and reduction in back pressure gave an appreciable power increment, of which operating and footplate staffs took immediate advantage, though the 5XP classification was retained until July 1943, when it became 6P and made the two engines equal officially to the unrebuilt Royal Scots.

Both engines were sent first to Leeds and worked thence to Glasgow over the Settle and Carlisle line and ex-GSWR route, and also

south-west from Leeds to Bristol. The standard of their performance on those duties led directly to sanction being given to the rebuilding of a second ten Royal Scots with the 2A boiler, and the locomotive committee minutes justified this conversion in 1943 on the ground that the weight would be reduced sufficiently to permit of use over the Leeds-Glasgow route, then carrying heavy war traffic. *Comet* and *Phoenix* were transferred in 1943 to Camden depot and for several years worked top-class Western Division passenger trains.

The first ten Royal Scot conversions had been authorised on 17 March 1942 before the two Jubilee rebuilds were at work, and before Stanier was seconded, so to him should be given the credit of sponsoring the Rebuilt Royal Scot design, perhaps the supreme 4-6-0 in British railway history.

LMSR post-war locomotive standardisation plans, announced in 1946, envisaged rebuilding and up-grading of all Patriot and Jubilee 5XP engines on the lines of Nos. 5735-36. A start was made by authorising the conversion of eighteen

Patriots, which became Class 6P as they re-appeared in 1946-49. However, no further conversions of either Patriots or Jubilees were undertaken in view of the imminent appearance of the BR new standard classes. The similar conversions of the Royal Scots were allowed to continue under the third LMSR authorisation, dated 19 July 1944, covering conversion of the last fifty engines of the class at an estimated cost of £237,000, but not until 1955 was the last of the seventy Royal Scots actually remodelled.

All these Royal Scot, Patriot and Jubilee rebuilds were up-graded to 7P in 1951 on the new BR formula. The 2A boiler was common to all ninety locomotives, and nine spare boilers were built down to 1953, all ninety-nine at Crewe. The two rebuilt Jubilees Nos. 5735-36 could, of course, use any of these boilers. No new locomotive was ever fitted with the 2A boiler. Smoke deflector plates were fitted alongside the smokeboxes of *Comet* and *Phoenix* around 1950, and they were the only two Jubilees to be so equipped. Both engines were withdrawn in 1966.

CHAPTER FOUR

THE BLACK FIVES

Most numerous of 20th Century British locomotive types to work wholly within the country was the LMSR Class 5 mixed-traffic 4-6-0 introduced in 1934, yet it was never the most numerous class on that Group system during the company's separate existence, being outnumbered by the 772 Midland-type 0-6-0s of Class 4F. Orders in hand on 1 January 1948, and engines included in the LMSR 1949 programme and confirmed by British Railways (BR), swelled the Class 5 total to 842, built from 1934 to 1951,

a number that exceeded both the ex-Midland 4F series and the 733 WD-type 2-8-0s (Nos. 90000 to 90732) purchased by BR in 1948. Additionally, the Class 5 design was adopted as the broad base for the standard Class 5MT 4-6-0 of series 73000, of which 172 were constructed by BR over the years 1951-57.

In the history of the British railway system the Class 5 total was exceeded only by the 943 Ramsbottom DX-class 0-6-0s built for the LNWR and LYR over the years 1858-74, but in

TABLE X DETAILS OF ORDERS FOR LMSR CLASS 5 4—6—0 LOCOMOTIVES

Date of authorisation	Year of introduction	No of locos	LMSR Lot No	Builder	Works order No	Works Nos	Sanctioned cost /loco & tender £
4/1934	1935	20	114	Crewe	377	216—35	6,500
1933	1934—5	50	119	Vulcan Fdy	(2)	4565—4614	(3)
6/1934	1935	5	122	Crewe	393	236—40	6,150
6/1934	1935	50	123	Vulcan Fdy	(2)	4618—4667	6,150
11/1934	1935	100	124	Armstrong Whitworth	—	1166—1265	5,119
1/1936	1936—7	227	131	Armstrong, Whitworth	—	1280—1506	6,080
5/1937	1938	20	142	Crewe	405	—	6,500
					406	—	6,500
1/1938	1943—4	35	151	Derby	0—3836	—	6,425
			152	Derby	0—4141	—	6,425
			153	Derby	0—4888	—	6,425
6/1943	1943—4	65	170	Derby	0—8263	—	9,500
				Crewe	453	—	9,500
				Crewe	454	—	9,500
				Crewe	455	—	9,500
				Crewe	456	—	9,500
				Crewe	457	—	9,500
11/1943	1945—6	95	174	Crewe	458	—	9,500
				Crewe	459	—	9,500
				Crewe	460	—	9,500
				Horwich	95	—	9,500
				Horwich	96	—	9,500
11/1944	1946—7	30	183	Crewe	463	—	9,575
				Horwich	97	—	9,575 (4)
12/1945	1947—8	65	187	Horwich	98	—	10,538 (4)
				Horwich	99	—	10,538 (4)
				Crewe	466	—	10,538 (4)
				Crewe	467	—	10,538 (4)
				Crewe	468	—	10,538 (4)
				Crewe	469	—	10,538 (4)
10/1946	1948—9	40	192	Horwich	102	—	10,125 (4)
				Crewe	472	—	10,125 (4)
10/1947	1949—51	40	199	Crewe	473	—	14,175 (4)
				Horwich	105	—	14,175 (4)

(1) In order of initial attachment to locomotives listed; (2) VF internal orders were 1420, 1425, 1430 for locomotives Nos 5020—69; 1740, 1745, 1750 for locomotives Nos 4075—5124; (3) Actual date of authorisation and sanctioned cost not known; (4) Actual costs:— No 44658 £12,280, Nos 44659—67 £12,101, Nos 44668—77 £14,748, Nos 44678—85 £16,235, Nos 44686/7 £20, 642, Nos 44688—95 £15,018, Nos 44696/7 £16,424, Nos 44698—44717 £14,450, Nos 44718—27 £11,580, Nos 44728—37 £11,826, Nos 44738—47 £13, 470, Nos 4748—54 £14,941, Nos 4755—7 £15,325, Nos 4758—64 £13,127, Nos 4765/6 £13,440, No 4767 £13,728, Nos 4768—82 £10,646, Nos 4783—99 £13,413, Nos 4982—96 £12,903, Nos 4997—9 £13, 413

the history of British locomotive construction the Class 5 total was exceeded also by the 852 Stanier-type Class 8F 2-8-0s and the 935 WD-type 2-8-0s. Many of the former and all of the latter were built to Ministry of War Transport orders, and in neither case were all allocated to British lines.

The DX engines all came from one works, Crewe, whereas the Stanier 2-8-0s came from ten works and the WD 2-8-0s from three. The LMSR Class 5 total involved three railway works and two private builders in a sequence of sixteen orders, of which six were each split among two works, so that in effect there were twenty-two orders. The private builders—Vulcan Foundry (VF) and Armstrong Whitworth (AW)— contributed 50½ per cent of the total, and the

second of the two orders to AW formed the largest single locomotive contract ever placed by a British railway, covering 227 locomotives and tenders of an aggregate empty weight of 207,000 tons, at a cost of £1,380,160, equivalent to £6080 apiece or £67 per ton. This large order placed at one time, with quick delivery promised, was possible financially through a government guaranteed loan under the Railways (Agreement) Act of 20 December 1935.

Class 5 was never so highly standardised as the DX or WD types. Apart from normal progress in details, from 1936 two boiler-firebox types were in use and they were not interchangeable. In later years also, major variations in valve gear and axleboxes were applied to about 5 per cent of the total number, and a different locomotive wheelbase was given to 110 engines, with corresponding increase in engine-plus-tender wheelbase and overall length. Moreover axle load rose from 18 tons at the beginning to a maximum of 19.45 tons in 1948.

Colloquially the LMSR type was known as the 'Black Five' from the combination of colour and power classification, but in early years it was often called the 'Black Stanier' to distinguish it from the red three-cylinder Jubilees. It was an attempt to fulfil the demands of the dominant operating department of the LMSR that had been crystallised first by J. H. Follows, operating superintendent, in 1923-24 for 'an engine that would go anywhere and do anything', changed in phraseology by the time of Stanier to the need for a 'universal' locomotive. The measure of the Black Five's success in this field was that it could run over 70 per cent of the LMSR route mileage and work approximately the same proportion of passenger and freight trains.

Its mixed-traffic basis was emphasised by the original power classification of 5P5F, that is class 5 power for both passenger and freight working. Only one other LMSR type, the Horwich Crab 2-6-0, had this double classification. From the first war-time repaints, around 1940, 5P5F was eliminated from the cab sides and replaced simply by the figure 5. Nevertheless the engines continued to do much passenger work, and in the immediate post-war years their large-scale use on principal passenger trains was one of the leading locomotive causes of the chronic unpunctuality of the LMSR Western and Midland Divisions, for they were much overloaded by train weights and speeds relative

LMSR/BR running Nos	Tender Nos (1)
5000—19	9002/54—64/7—72, 9164/5
5020—69	9074—9123
5070—4	9166—8, 9000/1
5075—5124	9169—9218
5125—5224	9229—9328
5225—5451	9461—9687
5452—61	9708—17
5462—71	9718—27
5472—81	9818—27
5482—96	9828—42
5497—9, 4800—6	9843—52
4807—25	10432—50
4826—35	10451—60
4836—45	10461—70
4846—55	10471—80
4856—65	10481—90
4866—71	10491—6
4872—91	10497—10516
4892—4911	10517—36
4912—31	10537—56
4932—41	10557—66
4942—66	10567—89, 10611, 10591
4967—81	10592—10606
4982—96	10607—10, 10590, 10612—21
4997—9, 4783—9	10670—9
4790—9	10680—9
4768--82	10625—39
4758—67	10640—9
4748—57	10650—9
44738—47	10660—9
44698—44717	10690—10709
44718—37	10710—29
44658—67	10798—10807
44668—97	10808—16, 10837, 10818—36
	10817

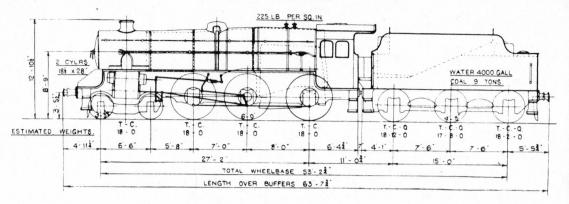

225 LB PER SQ. IN

2 CYLRS
18¼ x 28"

WATER 4000 GALL
COAL 9 TONS

ESTIMATED WEIGHTS.

T.C.	T.C.	T.C.	T.C.	T.C.Q	T.C.Q	T.C.Q
18-0	18-0	18-0	18-0	18-12-0	17-8-0	18-2-0

TOTAL WHEELBASE 53'-2¾"

LENGTH OVER BUFFERS 63'-7¼"

Above: **Fig 14** Diagram of first twenty Crewe-built Black Fives (1935) with estimated weights, which proved high.

Right: Domeless Black Five backing the TPO on to the southbound afternoon Mail at Dingwall, February 1939. Engines operating on the Highland section carried the small snow-clearers throughout the winter. *(Brian Reed)*

to general mechanical condition and standard of handling.

Class 5 was the fourth distinctive standard model evolved under Stanier, being preceded by 2-6-0s, 4-6-2s and three-cylinder 4-6-0s; and as related in Chapter 1 finance already sanctioned for other proposals was diverted to the construction of the first engines.

Despite early traffic experiences with the preceding types, the first fifty-seven Class 5 locomotives embodied Stanier's Swindon ideas of low-temperature superheat with fourteen flues and sets of elements in two rows; the elements were of bifurcated form and were not the triple single-pass small-bore elements favoured on the GWR. As with the other types, new tube and three-row flue layouts were needed after a few months to get additional super-heating surface and free gas area.

Even then the class did not settle down to a rigidly-controlled standard design. Still further changes in firebox size and in tube number and length were made. Along with variations in equipment, axleboxes, frames, wheel balancing and works procedure these helped to keep the class in the front rank mechanically, and enabled it to withstand the variations in driving and maintenance found in different links and depots spread over a system covering an area 700 miles north to south and 200 miles east to west, and to some extent to absorb the marked deterioration in handling and maintenance during and after World War II.

As in general the design followed concepts already put into practice, and had details of

similar form to those found in preceding Stanier locomotives, a decision was made to obtain a considerable number straight off the reel, and the initial order to Crewe for twenty was followed immediately by a contract with VF for fifty. Running numbers of the Crewe-built engines were 5000-19, but the VF engines, Nos. 5020-69 were all delivered before the first locomotive from Crewe was completed in February 1935. In 1934 a further five locomotives were ordered from Crewe and a second fifty from VF. The latter took the place of the thirty Jubilees at first proposed for outside builders, but transferred to Crewe as related in Chapter 2. Additionally, the first of the big AW contracts was placed, comprising one hundred engines and tenders.

Locomotive running numbers of these three orders, extending from 5070 to 5224, are detailed in Table X. To preserve this numbering sequence intact, many Western Division (ex-LNWR) engines bearing numbers in the same range were renumbered by the addition of 20000 in accordance with the LMSR re-numbering policy sanctioned earlier in 1934. AW deliveries began in April 1935 and were completed by the end of the year.

The next order placed was that with AW in January 1936 for the 227 engines already mentioned. Of these, Nos. 5225-98 were delivered in 1936 and Nos 5299-5451 in 1937. These locomotives had a revised sloping-throatplate boiler and firebox design with 24-element superheaters, and this revised design was followed in a subsequent order to Crewe for

twenty engines (Nos. 5452-71) completed near the end of 1938, but with a further increase in superheater elements to twenty-eight. This construction brought the pre-war Class 5 total up to 472, the yearly completion totals being: 1934 46; 1935 179; 1936 74; 1937 153; and 1938 30.

By the end of 1938 Stanier had provided the LMSR with over 1200 new locomotives, tender and tank, of efficient modern design. The 1939-40 programmes, as authorised before war changed LMSR locomotive requirements, seemed to indicate that most of the needs had been met, that the rate of new construction would slow down, with no large orders, and that Crewe would build all the steam locomotives, leaving Derby to deal with new diesel shunters and other work.

Concentration on war material and 2-8-0 freight engines deferred further Class 5 construction until 1943, when three contracts totalling thirty-five engines were placed on Derby works, which of Stanier-type tender engines had so far built only the ten Jubilees Nos. 5655-64. These contracts had been included in the 1939 programme for manufacture at Crewe, and the cost given in Table X is the expenditure sanctioned in 1939 and not the actual cost in 1943, which would be substantially more. When part of the third contract was complete the running numbers, hitherto in unbroken sequence from 5000, reached 5499, and as other modern 4-6-0s (the Patriots) already bore Nos. 5500 onwards, sequential numbering for the Black Fives was restarted at 4800.

Above: Front end of the first Class 5 to be built at Crewe, completed February 1935. Train-heating hose below buffer beam. This picture also shows how the front end was cut to clear station platforms on curves, first by the narrowing from 8ft 6½in to 7ft 8in at the drop in the running plate, and then by cutting off the bottom corners of the buffer beam. *(J. B. Radford collection)*

Above: Cab layout of sloping-throatplate domed-boiler locomotive No. 5268 built by AW in 1936. Photograph dates from April 1938, when the sand gun (just above the firedoor) had been added. The deep front windows were an improvement on the lights common on LMSR big-boiler locomotives prior to 1930. *(J. B. Radford collection)*

Right: **Fig 15** Diagram of sloping-throatplate domed-boiler Class 5 of the second AW order, Nos. 5225-5451, of 1936-37.

Below: One of the first 50 VF Class 5s after the original domeless boiler had been given a dome in the late 1930s. Tender still with the close spacing of LMS; engine still with gravity sanding, automatic de-sander and vacuum pump. *(D. G. Ritson collection)*

Before the end of the war Derby, Crewe and Horwich were all building Class 5 engines, including a batch of ninety-five of which only eighty had when ordered (November 1943) received the necessary sanction of the Ministry of War Transport. Class 5 construction continued through 1947-48 at Crewe and Horwich. Running numbers then reached 4999, and again a backward pass had to be made, beginning at 4758 and going on until 4799 was reached. By that time BR was in being and 40000 was added to the numbers of LMSR locomotives, but again backward sequence had to be adopted for further deliveries as indicated in Table X. The lowest number of all was 44658, while the last to be built was 44687, completed at Horwich in May 1951. Of the grand total of 842 only 748 actually bore LMSR numbers; the other ninety-four bore only BR numbers.

War-time construction was based on the revised sloping-throatplate boiler structure of 1936 with the twenty-eight flues of 1938, plus minor changes in frames and other details. Post-war construction, under H. G. Ivatt, the last chief mechanical engineer of the LMSR, was again modified, as were the designs of other classes, to promote greater mileage between overhauls, and less maintenance, inspection and disposal work between-whiles. This led to several new standard fittings and appliances, and to extended trial of roller-bearing axleboxes and poppet-valve gear. Completion of the first ten engines with roller bearings was achieved before the LMSR disappeared at the end of 1947, but most came after the formation of BR. The LMSR locomotive programme for 1948-49, drawn up in 1947, included a further eighty Class 5 engines, and this programme was left unaltered by BR (see Table X).

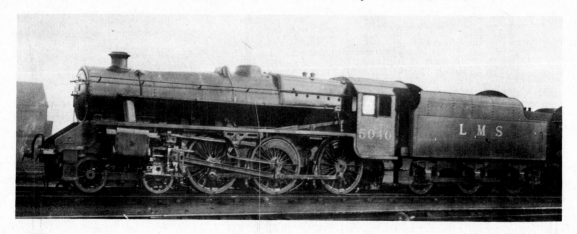

Initial Class 5 design embodied all the practices, many new to the LMSR, introduced by Stanier from 1932, including domeless taper boiler, Churchward curved-plate Belpaire firebox, 100 per cent direct staying of the firebox roof, sliding regulator on the saturated-steam side of the superheater header, GWR standard 225 lb/sq in boiler pressure, top feed, 2 per cent nickel-steel boiler shell plates except for the smokebox tubeplate, 3¾in water space at the foundation ring, jumper blastpipe top, long-lap long-travel piston valves of comparatively large diameter, strong wheels with triangular-section rims and swelled bosses without dishing, separate balance weights in the wheels, Gibson retaining rings for the tyres, large axle journals (here 8½in by 11in) with cast-steel boxes having pressed-in brasses and white metal inserts, 3in hollow bore through the coupled axles, manganese-molybdenum steel driving and coupling rods, side-bearer bogies (derived initially on the GWR from the de Glehn compound Atlantic of 1903, and which became known as 'French bogies' on the LMSR thirty years later), double-window cab with backward extension of the roof and tip-up wooden seats, and the new curved-top high-sided tender with self-trimming bunker. There were also several small 'Swindon' details such as brake blocks set normal to the tyre tread taper, thus involving angular setting of the brake cross beam and hanger bracket ends.

Pre-Stanier LMSR details retained were the crosshead-driven vacuum pump acting as a small ejector, vacuum-controlled steam brake on engine and tender, boiler-back fittings, and the live and exhaust steam injectors. A sand gun above the firedoor, with its five-charge hopper on the fireman's side of the cab, though an existing LMSR detail, was not fitted to the early Class 5s but came later, with Nos. 5452-71 of 1938. Train-heating connections front and back were on all engines.

All boilers fitted to Class 5 engines from beginning to end were classified as 3B. As explained in Chapter 2, the firebox was smaller than that of the 3A fitted to the Jubilees; but the barrel diameters and plate thicknesses were the same as those of the fifty nickel-steel 3A boilers of the fifty NBL-built Jubilees (see Chapter 2). Like the 3A, the 3B boilers were built in two major categories—domeless vertical-throatplate and domed sloping-throatplate, and they went through approximately the same superheater and tube changes, though Class 5 engines as a whole were never so sensitive to variations in firing and handling as the Jubilees.

Nos. 5000-06 and 5020-69 had the original vertical-throatplate domeless 3B boiler with 14-element superheater and two rows of 5⅛in flues. The second batch of orders, covering Nos. 5070-5224 from three works, followed Nos. 5007-19 of the first Crewe batch in retaining the same boiler structure but with a 21-element superheater with the flues in three rows; as before, the elements were bifurcated. These two boiler groups were interchangeable; they had a barrel length of 13ft 10½in, a length between tubeplates of 14ft 3in, a grate area of 27.8sq ft, and the grate bars were set to slope over the forward half and were horizontal over the rear half.

With the 227 locomotives ordered from AW at the beginning of 1936 was introduced the sloping-throatplate variation. Outside diameters at front and back of barrel were retained, but the throatplate was inclined forward about 10½in from the foundation ring, and resulted in

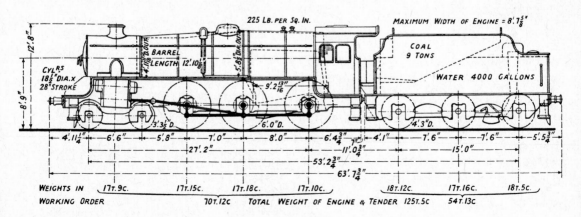

One of the 227 AW locomotives of 1936-37 with which
the then new sans insignia were introduced to Class 5.
Sloping-throatplate domed boiler; steam sanding.
(J. B. Radford collection)

12in shorter barrel and tube length, though
overall barrel and firebox length remained the
same, as did the 6ft 8in smokebox length. The
taper ring was unaltered; only the front ring was
shortened. To suit the shorter length the tube
diameter was reduced from 2in to 1⅞in. All
these locomotives, Nos. 5225-5451, had
24-element superheaters with 5⅛in flues in three
rows and 159 tubes of 1⅞in o.d., that is, the
same as the final standard arrangement in the
3A Jubilee boilers, and the final standard of the
vertical-throatplate 3B boilers in the earlier
Class 5s.

Firebox heating surface rose by 9.5 per cent to
171sq ft, and the firebox volume increased to
about 170cu ft, or about 60 per cent the volume
of a Duchess Pacific firebox. As with the 3A, the
grate area was increased slightly by reduction in
foundation ring width to 3in, and the flat rear
section of the grate was shortened, producing a
longer and flatter slope at the front. Three sets
of firebars were used from front to back in place
of two long sets. Also as in the 3A, the sloping
throatplate version had a dome on the back ring
housing a sliding-type regulator; and the
top-feed remained in the same position on the
back ring but had a narrower casing than the
original. Two staggered handholes per side were
added to the top corner of the outer firebox.

In Crewe-built Nos. 5452-71 of 1938 this
sloping-throatplate domed construction was
retained, but a four-row 28-element superheater
was adopted that gave 54 per cent more
superheating surface than the original
14-element model, and there was only a slight
reduction in the number of tubes to 151 (see
Fig 16—due to E. S. Cox). Otherwise the only
boiler change was a thickening of the upper part
of the firebox tubeplate by ⅛in that reduced the
distance between tubeplates by a like amount.
This thicker tubeplate was put on earlier engines
on renewal. Though by 1938 the smokebox
deflector plates and jumper tops were being
removed in the sheds, the twenty engines of 1938
were given them when new. All variations in the
3B boiler are included in Table XI, and at the
foot of that table will be found details of changes
in superheater element thickness and
corresponding alterations in superheating
surface.

The disadvantage of this sloping-throatplate
boiler was that it was not interchangeable with
the vertical-throatplate type fitted to the first
225 Black Fives. Those locomotives had to retain
their original boilers, but from 1937 the
fifty-seven boilers that had 14-element superheaters when new were equipped gradually with
24-element superheaters (see second line of
Table XI). At the same time steam domes were
put on those fifty-seven boilers and the regulator
was altered; the top feed remained in the same
position. The original 12in greater barrel length,

TABLE XI 3B BOILER HEATING SURFACE VARIATION CLASS 5 4–6–0

Foot note ref	Tubes No/Dia (inches)	Flues No/Dia (inches)	Heating surface sq ft	Superheater No/Dia (inches)	elements SWG	Superheater surface sq ft	Firebox heating surface sq ft	Grate area sq ft	Free gas area sq ft
(a)	160/2	14/5 1/8	1463	14/1 3/8	11	228	156	27.8	3.90
(b)	159/1 7/8	24/5 1/8	1570	24/1 1/4	11	331	156	27.8	4.55
(c)	138/2	21/5 1/8	1441	21/1 1/4	11	270	156	27.8	4.20
(d)	136/2	21/5 1/8	1426	21/1 1/4	11	270	156	27.8	4.15
(e)	159/1 7/8	24/5 1/8	1459	24/1 1/4	11	307	171	28.65	4.55
(f)	151/1 7/8	28/5 1/8	1479	28/1 3/4	11	359	171	28.65	4.70
(g)	151/1 7/8	28/5 1/8	1479	28/1 3/8	11	376	171	28.65	4.50
(h)	151/1 7/8	28/5 1/8	1479	28/1 1/4	11	348	171	28.65	4.70
(j)	151/1 7/8	28/5 1/8	1479	28/1 3/8	9	365	171	28.65	4.50

Vertical throatplate boilers: notes (a) to (d).
Sloping throatplate boilers: notes (e) to (j).
(a) Nos 5000–6, 5020–69 as built; (b) boilers in (a) rebuilt with domes; (c) Nos 5007–19, 5070–99, 5100–4, 5125–74 as built; (d) Nos 5105–24, 5175–5224 as built: boilers in (c) altered to this arrangement but all remained domeless; (e) Nos 5225–5451 as built; (f) Nos 5452–71 as built; (g) Nos 5472–99 and 4800–4920 as built; (h) Nos 4921–99, 44698–44717 and 44738–99 as built; (j) Nos 44718–37 and 44658–97 as built: the 1 3/8 in 9 SWG elements then became standard for renewals.

Variations of superheating surface (3A and 3B boilers):

Elements: od/SWG	1 3/8 /11	1 1/8 /13	1 1/8 /11	1 1/4 /11	1 3/8 /9
No of elements 14	228	—	—	—	—
21	—	270	235	270 (1)	(3)
			256 (2)	290 (2)	(3)
24	—	—	—	307 (1)	(3)
				331 (2)	313 (2)
28	376	—	312	348 (1)	365 (1)
				359 (1)	

(1) 3B boiler in Class 5; (2) 3A boiler in Jubilee; (3) Not given on diagrams but by calculation (same length elements) would have been 273 sq ft for 21 elements and 313 for 24 elements.

vertical-throatplate, and the 55:45 ratio of slope and flat of the grate remained. The vertical-throatplate boilers built originally with 21-element superheaters were never rebuilt with domes, but of course remained interchangeable with the altered boilers in the same group.

Alteration of the first 225 engines to take the sloping-throatplate boiler was possible in the shops by moving further forward the steel-plate frame cross stay in front of the throatplate. No spare boilers had been ordered for those locomotives, and when from 1937 some became desirable to get engines out of Crewe repair shops more quickly, thirteen boilers were set aside as such and the engines from which they were taken were modified in the frames to take the sloping-throatplate shape and provided with such boilers, built under spares orders. The locomotives concerned were Nos. 5002/20/2/3/ 6/7/40/7/54/7/8/97 and 5142. The work was done in 1937-38 without specific locomotive-committee sanction, and to regularise matters retrospective authorisation was minuted on 30 October 1941, and this covered also the similar work in relation to the 3A boilers and Jubilees described in Chapter 2.

All spare boilers built new as such were of

sloping-throatplate domed type and weighed 17.82 tons empty but complete with mountings. Twenty-two spare boilers were built to two orders in 1937-38 with 24-element superheaters, and another forty-two with 28-element superheaters in nine orders from then on until 1960. All boilers for railway-built locomotives and all spares were manufactured at Crewe, whatever works was responsible for the engines. The private makers built the boilers for the 427 locomotives they supplied.

Altogether 906 nickel-steel boilers were made for the 842 locomotives, giving 7½ per cent spares; they came to be comprised of: 57 vertical-throatplate domeless boilers rebuilt with domes; 168 vertical-throatplate domeless boilers never rebuilt; 617 domed sloping-throatplate boilers built for locomotive orders; and 64 domed sloping-throatplate boilers built as spares and replacements.

To keep down axle load and ensure the original wide route availability, all 3B boilers had shells of nickel steel, even for war-time construction when alloy steels were at a premium. This steel could be flanged easily and could be electric arc-welded. It saved about a ton in the weight of a Class 5. It contained 1.75

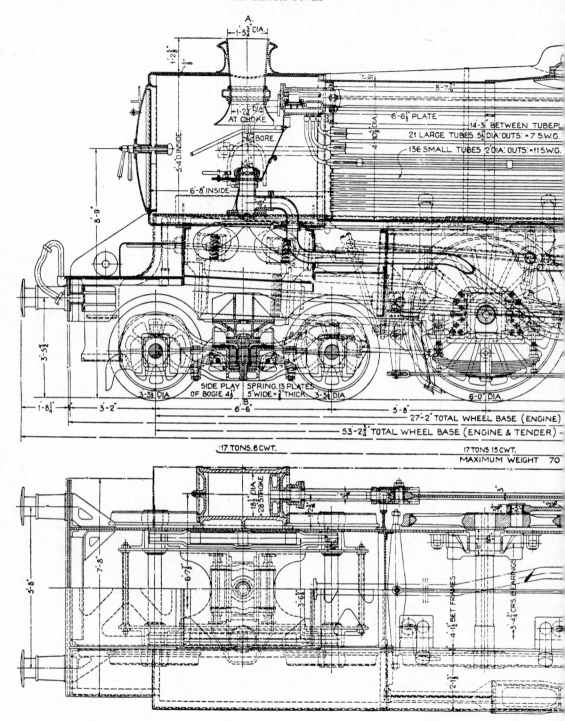

Fig 15a General arrangement (elevation and plan) of
21-element superheater vertical-throatplate domeless-
boiler Class 5 locomotive.

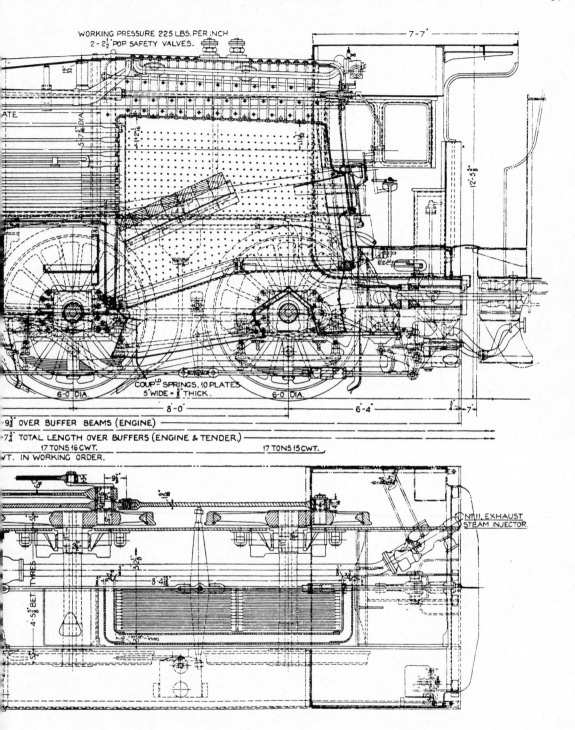

WORKING PRESSURE 225 LBS. PER INCH
2 - 2½" POP SAFETY VALVES.

7'-7"

12'-5⅝"

COUP⁰ SPRINGS. 10 PLATES.
5" WIDE × ⅝" THICK.

6'-0 DIA.

6'-0 DIA.

8'-0"

6'-4"

¾"

7"

9½" OVER BUFFER BEAMS (ENGINE)

7½" TOTAL LENGTH OVER BUFFERS (ENGINE & TENDER.)

17 TONS 16 CWT.

17 TONS 15 CWT.

WT. IN WORKING ORDER.

No.11. EXHAUST STEAM INJECTOR.

8'-4⅞"

4'-5⅝" BET. TYRES

0   1   2   3   4 FT

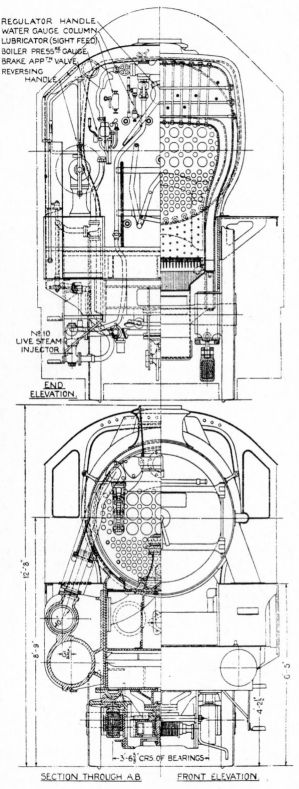

REGULATOR HANDLE
WATER GAUGE COLUMN
LUBRICATOR (SIGHT FEED)
BOILER PRESS.RE GAUGE
BRAKE APP.TN VALVE
REVERSING
HANDLE

Nº 10
LIVE STEAM
INJECTOR

END
ELEVATION.

12'-8"

8'-9"

6'-5"

4'-2½"

⊢3'-6⅜"CRS. OF BEARINGS⊣

SECTION THROUGH A.B.   FRONT ELEVATION.

Left: **Fig 15b** General arrangement (end views and sections) of 21-element superheater vertical-throatplate domeless-boiler Class 5 locomotive.

Right: **Fig 16** Final tube and flue layout for 3B boilers in Black Fives built 1938 and onwards; 28 flues and 151 tubes.

to 2 per cent of nickel, 0.20/0.25 per cent of carbon, 0.10/0.15 per cent of silicon, 0.50/0.75 per cent of manganese, and not more than 0.04 per cent each of sulphur and phosphorus. Required tensile strength was 34/38ton/sq in with a yield point of 17/19ton/sq in, and an elongation of 22/24 per cent with a 50 per cent reduction in area.

In a noticeable respect Stanier permitted a departure from one of the most rigid of Swindon practices: the 18½in by 28in cylinders of the Class 5 were set at a slope of 1 in 24. Swindon under Churchward, Collett and Hawksworth never departed from the horizontal for outside cylinders, and even put the centre line 2½in above axle centre to maintain that location and give enough clearance for bogie wheels and pony trucks. Piston thrust was 60,500lb.

Inside-admission piston valves were 10in diameter, or 54 per cent of the cylinder bore. Stanier did not insist on the Swindon semi-plug type of head and used the LMSR multi-rings for sealing, but he did allow the long-established Swindon lap-lead ratio of 12 or 14:1 to be changed to 7:1. Steam and exhaust pipes were free and direct, and the 5¼in blast nozzle with Churchward jumper top was set 7in below boiler centre line. In the first fifty VF locomotives the exhaust branches were cast in with the smokebox saddle, but in immediately subsequent engines the exhaust branches and saddle were part of a much more substantial cast steel cross-stay structure, and later again became separate steel castings.

In general, the Walschaerts motion gave a maximum travel of 6.47in, with 1.67in maximum port opening (front) and 1.8in (back), corresponding to 76 and 72.5 per cent cut-off. At 20 per cent cut-off travel was 3.52in but port opening to steam was no more than 0.28in. Lead was constant at 0.275in front port and 0.226in back port. Steam lap was 1½in, and $\frac{1}{16}$in exhaust clearance was provided. Cylinder clearance was about 9.5 per cent. From No. 5452

Right: **Fig 17** Cylinder and valve chest casting of Black Fives, 1938.

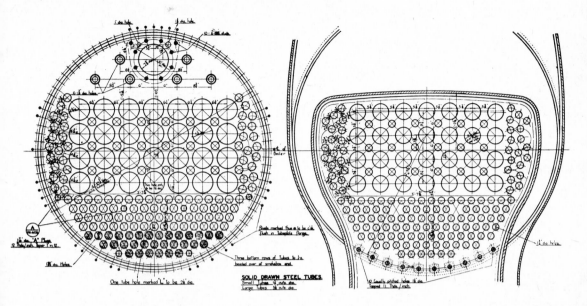

some engines had needle roller bearings for some of the motion pins. In common with other Stanier classes, cut-off when coasting was enjoined at 45 per cent, and there was a mark at this point on the reversing sector plate; drivers were instructed to keep the regulator 'fractionally open' under such conditions.

Main frame plates were 1in thick in the first 225 engines and $1\frac{1}{16}$in thick from No. 5225 onwards, until with Nos. 4997-99 in 1947 $1\frac{1}{8}$in was adopted and used for all subsequent locomotives numbered below 4800. The rear

horn clips were cross-tied by two inverted T-sections, but in the first 225 engines these were considered eventually to have increased the number of cracks round the *leading* horn gaps (Cox, Institution of Locomotive Engineers), and in those engines the number of frame cracks per locomotive per year increased steadily to four over the first eight years. From January 1939 until 1945 many engines were given a cross-stay at the leading coupled axlebox guides to try and stop frame distortion.

The 6ft 6in-wheelbase side-bearer bogie was

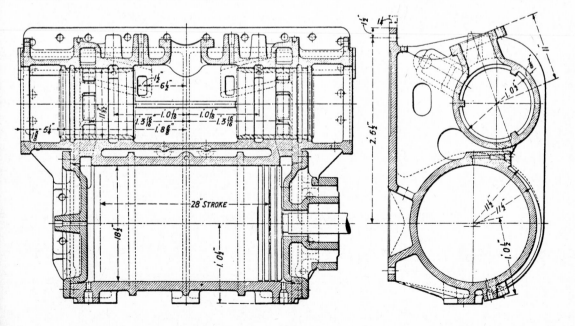

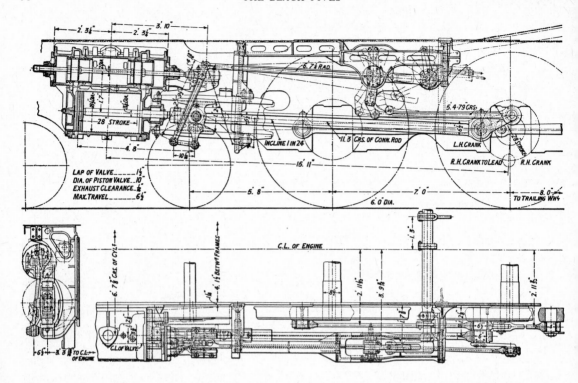

standard with that of the 27ft 7in-wheelbase Jubilees. Side bearers with hemispherical cups were supported on inverted laminated springs at 3ft 6⅝in transverse centres, and the lateral movement of 2¼in each way was cushioned by two coil springs in parallel.

Six sandboxes were carried to provide front sanding to the first and second coupled wheel pairs and back sanding to the third pair. The forward four boxes were within the frames and had 3ft 0in filling necks brought up above running plate level. Sand ejection in the first 225 engines was by gravity. A duo-directional automatic hot-water de-sander was introduced, as at that time the LMSR was having some trouble with track circuits and sand on the rails was thought to affect regular operation. From No. 5225 onwards steam sanding replaced the trickle type, and no de-sanders were fitted.

Distinct from the Jubilees, the two mechanical lubricators (one of twelve feeds for cylinders, valves and glands and the other of eight feeds for the coupled axleboxes) were both arranged on the right-hand running plate, and though well back from the driving wheel were driven from the top of the right-hand combination lever.

In essence the first seventy engines were the same, but not strictly so. Some, and probably all, of the first fifty of VF build had long chimneys and a height of 12ft 10½in above rails. Crewe-built Nos. 5000-19 had shorter chimneys giving a maximum height of 12ft 8in; this remained standard for new construction and the fifty VF engines gradually were supplied with the shorter pattern. The preliminary Class 5 layout prepared at Euston showed a stovepipe chimney, but this was altered under T. F. Coleman at Crewe to the shapely form already adopted for other Stanier classes, as Euston knew it would. Nos. 5020-35, if not others, had no curved casing below the smokebox door, but by the summer of 1937 they had been given it, as it was so convenient for getting at the smokebox door handles and upper lamp bracket. Succeeding engines had this casing from new.

Compared with the first Crewe and Vulcan locomotives the AW engines Nos. 5125-5224 had some visible detail modifications. For example the water delivery pipe to the top feed was within the boiler cleading sheets, whereas it was outside on the first seventy. There was also a difference in the attachment of the vacuum pump to the bottom slide bar.

No correct axle load and weight distribution diagrams and data for the first seventy engines

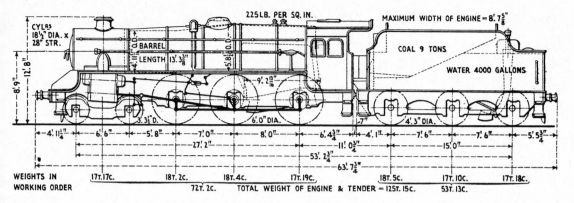

Left: **Fig 18** Arrangement of standard Walschaerts motion of Class 5 4-6-0.

Above: **Fig 19** Diagram of Black Fives of 1938-45 construction with 28-element four-row superheater.

Below: An early Ivatt modified Class 5 of 1947 with Timken roller-bearing axleboxes throughout engine and tender. Lined LMS insignia introduced in 1946. Top feed moved forward to front ring of barrel. I-section coupling rods.

were published; even the official diagrams showed only estimated weights, which were simply 18 tons on the bogie and 18 tons on each coupled axle, giving a working order total of 72 tons; but this was 2.9 tons less than the estimated weight of the first Euston design of 1932, which had 18.95 tons estimated maximum axle load.

True weights were given in the diagram of the first hundred AW engines, which had a maximum axle load of 17.8 tons, 53.15 tons of adhesion weight, and a locomotive weight of 70.6 tons. This total weight figure with only the slightest change in distribution was perpetuated for the sloping-throatplate variation that began with the 227 AW engines of 1936-37, and was continued for the twenty turned out of Crewe in

1938. The diagrams for all these engines showed weights, reading from the front, of 17.3, 17.75, 17.8 and 17.75 tons, a remarkably even distribution for a 4-6-0. Empty weight was 64.1 tons. By 1946, however, the weight of the 28-element superheater engines was given officially at 72.1 tons, with 18.2 tons maximum axle load, 54.25 tons adhesion weight, and 65.65 tons empty weight. A driving wheel-and-axle set scaled 4.27 tons, and so sprung weight on that axle was about 13.9 tons.

War-time engines from the three works had the 1938-revise 28-flue boiler but with different element diameter and thickness that altered the superheating surface. Apart from the top-feed being moved forward to the front ring of the barrel, the same design was followed in the first post-war bulk order (LMSR lot number 187, Table X), but these engines were given self-cleaning smokeboxes, hopper ashpans, link-and-pin cross stays at the horns, and manganese-steel liners to boxes and guides. Some of these fittings had come earlier, in particular, self-cleaning smokeboxes had been introduced with Nos. 4886-4920 in 1945; all engines so fitted had a small cast-iron plate 'SC' on the lower part of the smokebox door.

Further, out of a total of sixty-five engines in

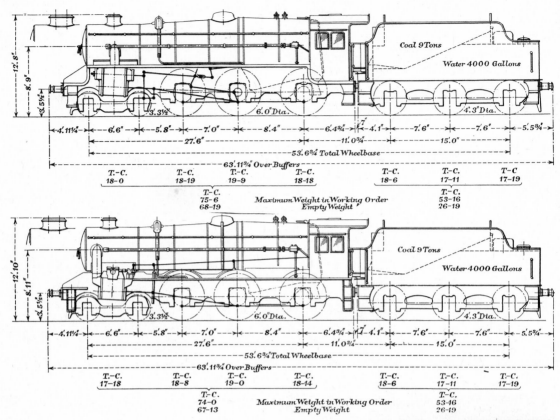

TABLE XII GENERAL DIMENSIONS OF PRINCIPAL LMSR & LMR CLASS VARIATIONS (1)

Locomotive numbers		5000—5070	5125—5224	5225—5451	5472—5499	4758—4766	4748—4757
Cylinders (2)	in	18 1/2 X 28	18 1/2 X 28	18 1/2 X 28	18 1/2 X 28	18 1/2 X 28	18 1/2 X 28
Wheel diam	in	72	72	72	72	72	72
Boiler pressure	psi	225	225	225	225	225	225
Coupled wheelbase	ft in	15—0	15—0	15—0	15—0	15—4	15—4
Engine wheelbase	ft in	27—2	27—2	27—2	27—2	27—6	27—6
No & od of tubes	in	160@2	136@2	159@1 7/8	151@1 7/8	151@1 7/8	151@1 7/8
No & od of flues	in	14@5 1/8	21@5 1/8	24@5 1/8	24@5 1/8	28@5 1/8	28@5 1/8
Free gas area	sq ft	3.90	4.15	4.55	4.70	4.70	4.70
Length between tubeplates	ft in	14—3	14—3	13—3	13—2 7/8	13—2 7/8	13—2 7/8
Evap H.S. — tubes & flues	sq ft	1463	1426	1459	1479	1479	1479
firebox	sq ft	156	156	171	171	171	171
total	sq ft	1619	1582	1630	1650	1650	1650
Type of firebox (3)		VT	VT	ST	ST	ST	ST
Grate area	sq ft	27.8	27.8	28.65	28.65	28.65	28.65
Superheating surface	sq ft	227	270	307	359	348	348
Max axle load	tons	18.0 (4)	17.8	17.9	18.2	19.45	19.0
Adhesion weight	tons	54.0 (4)	53.0	53.15	54.25	57.3	56.1
Locomotive weight wo	tons	72.0 (4)	70.0	70.6	72.1	75.3	74.0
Locomotive weight empty	tons	66.0 (4)	64.1	64.25	65.75	68.95	67.65
Boiler pitch	ft in	8—9	8—9	8—9	8—9	8—9	8—11
Max height of loco	ft in	12-10 1/2 (5)	12—8	12—8	12—8	12—8	12—10
Type of axlebox		Plain	Plain	Plain	Plain	Timken	Timken
Valves		Piston	Piston	Piston	Piston	Piston	Poppet
Valve motion		Walschaerts	Walschaerts	Walschaerts	Walschaerts	Walschaerts	Caprotti
Tender(2): tare	tons	27.25	27.25	26.8	26.8	26.95	26.95
laden weight	tons	54.1	53.65	53.65	53.65	53.8	53.8
tank type		Rivetted	Welded	Welded	Welded	W/R (6)	W/R (6)
Loco & tender wo weight	tons	126.1 (4)	123.65	124.25	125.75	129.1	127.8
Loco & tender wheelbase	ft in	53—2 3/4	53—2 3/4	53—2 3/4	53—2 3/4	53—6 3/4	53—6 3/4
Loco & tender over buffers	ft in	63—7 3/4	63—7 3/4	63—7 3/4	63—7 3/4	63—11 3/4	63—11 3/4

(1) Tractive effort of all types 25,455 lbs at 85% factor; (2) All tenders 4,000 gal water and 9 tons coal; (3) VT = vertical throatplate, ST = sloping throatplate; (4) Estimated; (5) 12—8 in Nos 5000—19; (6) Combined welded and rivetted.

Top left: **Fig 20** Diagram of Timken-axlebox Walschaerts-motion Ivatt-type Black Five of lengthened (27ft 6in) wheelbase, 1947-48.

Centre left: **Fig 21** Diagram of Timken-axlebox Caprotti-motion Ivatt-type Black Five of 27ft 6in wheelbase, 1947-48.

Left: Outside Stephenson motion, with launch-type expansion links, and double chimney of No. 4767 as completed at the end of 1947.

lot 187, ten engines (Nos. 44738-47) were given Caprotti valve motion and standard plain-bearing axleboxes; another ten (Nos. 4748-53 and 44754-57) were given Caprotti gear and Timken roller-bearing axleboxes throughout engine and tender; nine engines (Nos. 4758-66) had Timken boxes throughout and Walschaerts motion with piston valves; one engine (No. 4767) had outside Stephenson motion, piston valves, and Timken axleboxes throughout. Six locomotives (Nos. 44755-57, 4765-67) out of the thirty were provided with twin exhausts and double chimneys; of these, three had Caprotti gear and Timken boxes, two had Walschaerts motion and Timken boxes, and one was the Stephenson-motion engine. This last-named, with extra drawing office charges attached, cost £13,278, some £600 more than concurrent Walschaerts-motion engines with the same type of axlebox. The two mechanical lubricators, in the standard position, were driven in this engine by a rod attached to the rear end of the back-gear eccentric rod.

The double chimney and twin exhaust of No. 4767 were replaced by a single system in 1953 because of exhaust steam drift obscuring the driver's vision. The others retained their twin exhausts, and this system was also put on the last Black Five of all in 1951.

The other thirty-five engines of lot 187, including all twenty from Horwich, were largely to existing war-time standard except for the features noted three paragraphs above. Subsequently, in 1949-51, Nos. 44678-87 were given SKF parallel-roller bearings throughout, Nos. 44668-77 had SKF driving boxes only, and Nos. 44688-97 had Timken boxes on the driving axle only.

With the first Timken-fitted units came the first change in Black Five linear dimensions.

Above: Caprotti Black Five with plain-bearing axleboxes, completed early in 1948 and which never bore an LMSR number. Steel cylinder castings. Boiler pitch 2in above standard, and overall height to top of chimney also 2in more than standard. Open-work footsteps were peculiar to the Caprottis. *(R. T. Ellis collection)*

Below: Caprotti Class 5 with Timken roller bearings throughout. Insignia of transition form used for some engines early in 1948 with *M* denoting London Midland Region. Power classification shown by the small *5* below the cab-side number. Note difference in length of sandbox necks compared with those in preceding illustration. *(R. T. Ellis collection)*

Room for the big split cannon-type boxes could not be found with convenience around the firebox in the standard 7ft plus 8ft coupled wheel spacing, so the latter dimension was increased to 8ft 4in, giving a locomotive wheelbase of 27ft 6in against the normal 27ft 2in. Engine-plus-tender wheelbase and overall length were increased by like amounts. This modification was effected without change in boiler dimensions, but the smokebox was 4in longer.

Of LMSR lot number 187 (Table X), additional to the Timken-fitted locomotives, the Caprotti engines with plain bearings (Nos. 4738-47) also had the extended wheelbase, but Walschaerts-motion plain-bearing locomotives (Nos. 4768-99 and 4997-99) had the 27ft 2in wheelbase. Thereafter, for the two later LMSR lot numbers 192 and 199, totalling eighty engines, to simplify frame marking-off and

machining the extended 27ft 6in wheelbase was adopted as standard for all engines whether plain or roller bearings were applied, and in all these the longer smokebox was used. Table XIII summarises the position of these non-standard engines.

The Caprotti locomotives had cast-steel cylinders from the Crewe foundry, with cast-iron bushes pressed in, and the engines had two major differences in appearance. First, boiler pitch had to be raised 2in from the standard 8ft 9in and the overall height became 12ft 10in; the smokebox had to be lengthened and the chimney set forward to accommodate the Caprotti valve box and revised steam and exhaust pipe layout. Secondly, the running plate was lowered level with the top of the Caprotti valve box, and three separate splashers per side were needed.

A short separate running plate extended back

TABLE XIII LMSR/BR VARIATIONS IN CLASS 5 4—6—0

BR Locomotive Nos	Valve motion	Axlebox bearings	Locomotive wheelbase ft in
44658—67	Walschaerts	Plain	27—6
44668—77	Walschaerts	SKF driving axle	27—6
44678—85	Walschaerts	SKF all axles	27—6
44686/7 (3)	Caprotti (1)	SKF all axles	27—6
44688—97	Walschaerts	Timken driving axle	27—6
44698—44737	Walschaerts	Plain	27—6
44738—47	Caprotti (2)	Plain	27—6
44748—57 (3)	Caprotti (2)	Timken all axles	27—6
44758—66 (3)	Walschaerts	Timken all axles	27—6
44767 (3)	Stephenson	Timken all axles	27—6
44768—45499	Walschaerts	Plain	27—2

(1) Two outside drives; (2) Single central inside drive; (3) Double chimney Nos 44686/7, 44755—7/65—7 (removed from No 44767 in 8/1953).

some 40in from the front buffer beam. There was no drop at the back end of the running angle to give deep cab side sheets, but the interior height of the cab was not altered as the wooden deck in the standard model was between upper and lower running angle heights, and remained at the normal 5ft 4in above rails. Caprotti engine layout brought a difference between engine and tender running angle heights. Footsteps at front and back of the engine also were of a new open type. Caprotti boilers had a steam-actuating pipe connection from the lhs of the steam dome. Sandbox necks were of different lengths in Nos. 4738-47 to those in Nos. 4748-57.

The Caprotti gear itself had a single inside bevel gear and rotating shaft drive from the leading coupled axle, but the primary end of the drive in Timken-box engines had to differ from the standard bevel-and-spur on the axle by reason of the cannon axlebox, and had to have the gear carried on a top facing to that box. Reversing gear was unusual in that the screw wheel in the cab needed the same number of turns from full forward to full backward as the standard Walschaerts motion instead of only the single full turn that met Caprotti requirements. This was to make Class 5 variations more suited to common user.

Caprotti locomotives had a plate on the regulator handle instructing the driver to close the regulator while coasting. A practical working defect of the Caprottis as arranged on the LMSR was that they could not be reversed directly from or to an intermediate cut-off position, but first had to be moved to the full-gear position in the new direction required.

The last two of all Class 5s, Nos. 44686-87 from Horwich in 1951, were, at the instance of BR, provided with completely revised Caprotti installations with a rotating shaft drive on each side actuated by a worm gearbox on a flycrank on the driving axle and fitted with a self-locking worm-type reversing gear. Valve events also were different from those of the 1947-48 engines. No splashers were used in these two engines and the running plates were higher than in any other Class 5 engines. Partly because of high

TABLE XIV SCHEDULED FRAME AND SUSPENSION IMPROVEMENTS CARRIED OUT FROM 2/1951 TO 12/1958

Locomotive running Nos	5000—5461	5462—5471	5472—99, 4800—6/17—20/3, 4952	4807—16/21/2/4—99, 4900—21/32—51
Hornblocks and axleguides	X	X	—	Existing to be machined to take manganese-steel liners
Manganese steel liners	X	X	X	X
Horwich-type horn clips	X	X	X	X
Pin-jointed cross stays at horns	X	X	—	—
Spring brackets and details	X	—	—	—
Springs	X	—	—	—
Frame inserts	X	X	X	X

Strengthening plates first introduced in 1939 to be removed (where fitted)
New ashpan for locomotives with vertical throatplate boilers

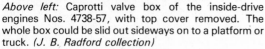

Above left: Caprotti valve box of the inside-drive engines Nos. 4738-57, with top cover removed. The whole box could be slid out sideways on to a platform or truck. *(J. B. Radford collection)*

Above right: Central valve-drive line of the Timken-Caprotti locomotives Nos. 4748-57, showing gear case on top of the cannon-type axlebox. Note long filling necks of forward sandboxes, with reversing shaft just in front.

Below: The last two Black Fives of all, Nos. 44686-87 of 1951, were equipped with revised Caprotti motion having an outside drive line on each side, and also had twin exhaust. BR standard black livery with red lining to boiler, cab, running angle and tender. Open-work footsteps as used in the earlier Caprottis.

development charges spread over only two locomotives, and partly because of advancing labour and material costs and the provision of SKF roller-bearing axleboxes throughout, these two engines, including tenders, cost £20,642 apiece, some £5000 more than the last two standard Class 5s going through Horwich works almost at the same time.

Though by the end of 1951 the twenty Caprottis of 1947-48 had aggregated above three million miles, they had certain difficulties in the drive, and others in the valve events, that made them rather slow accelerators through the lower speed range, though they had plenty of power at high speeds and also coasted freely. Most of the difficulties were obviated in Nos. 44686-87, and those two installations formed the base for the later Caprotti applications to certain BR Class 5MT engines. All Caprottis could be distinguished by the sharp crisp exhaust sound.

Timken-fitted locomotives of 1947-48 that retained Walschaerts motion and piston valves weighed 75.3 tons all on, and had a maximum axle load of 19.45 tons and an empty weight of 68.95 tons; nearly all the weight increase was due to the provision of roller bearings and cannon boxes. Weight of the Caprotti-Timkens was less at 74 tons in working order; maximum axle load was 19 tons and empty weight 67.65 tons. Caprotti engines with plain bearings

scaled 72.2 tons in working order and 65.85 tons empty. Engines that had Timken or SKF roller-bearing boxes to the driving axle only scaled 73.9 tons in working order and 67.55 tons empty and had a maximum axle load of 19.15 tons. The remaining engines with plain boxes and Walschaerts motion and 27ft 2in locomotive wheelbase were given as 72.6 tons, but similar engines with the new 27ft 6in wheelbase scaled 73.5 tons all on, 67.15 tons empty, and had 18.75 tons maximum axle load. The Stephenson-motion engine weighed 75.3 tons in working order and 68.95 tons empty, and maximum axle load was 19.45 tons.

Various detail modifications throughout the locomotives were made from 1937 onwards. Through 1938-40 the crosshead-driven vacuum pumps were gradually removed from Nos. 5000-5451; No. 5452 *et seq* never had them. From 1937 Nos. 5000-5224 gradually were provided with steam sanding in place of the trickle type, and from 1938 the de-sanders were removed, and may have been out of use for some time previously. Between 1939 and 1941 platform supports were strengthened on Nos. 5000-5471, and between 1939 and 1956 stiffening brackets for cab wing plates were added to Nos. 5000-5224. Brake valves were standardised from 1945 by replacing the Gresham type on Nos. 5000-5224 with the LMSR standard valve with separate ejector steam valve.

Intermediate buffing blocks between engine and tender were fitted when new to Nos. 5070 *et seq*, and were added to Nos. 5000-69 from 1948. Through the years various small frame modifications were made, of which the most important were the strengthened dragbox put in from 1943, and the decision in 1941 (reversed after ten years or so) to fit strengthening plates round the driving horn gaps. A few engines seem to have been given these strengthening plates from 1939.

From 1939 the intermediate back-facing ashpan damper was welded shut to minimise ash deposits on the adjacent axleboxes, and from 1938 new engines had a modified ashpan with curved base plate and no intermediate damper; steaming continued to be satisfactory after these modifications. From 1945 stronger bogie side control springs were put into Nos. 5000-5471 in an endeavour to improve riding; on the same engines new piston-head fastenings replaced the original Swindon-type screw-on connection at shop visits, though both pistons were not always

altered at the same time. The work of replacing the 10-plate coupled springs by others of sixteen thinner plates was begun in 1938 on Nos. 5000-5224. Fall plates between engine and tender had to be modified in 1939 to give certain clear passage on the sharpest curves in depots and sidings.

Originally Class 5 axleboxes had white metal linings bearing on the cast-steel guide face. Though these liners were by no means wear-less, the Stanier axlebox was a great improvement on the ex-Midland solid bronze box hitherto favoured on the LMSR, and by 1939 the 472 Black Fives then in traffic had suffered only fifty-four hot boxes in two years. Moreover there had been only eighteen hot big ends in the same period. Nevertheless, the thrust-face wear problem led to a trial with pegged-on bronze liners in Nos. 5472-99 and 4800-06 when new in 1943-44, but these often had to be renewed between shoppings because of excessive wear, and they were hardly as good as the white metal type.

Largely because of experience on the London Underground, which by 1944 was fitting manganese-steel liners to the thrust faces of every box on its trains as they came through the Acton shops, the LMSR introduced this method in preference to bronze and white metal liners on five Class 5 4-6-0s built in 1944, bedding and welding the liners on to the box before the brass was pressed in, and welding a liner to the horn surface with the interposition of a mild-steel backing plate.

After the first few thousand miles these showed a greatly reduced rate of wear and helped the original centre-to-centre distances, clearances, and 'squareness' to be almost maintained between shoppings, and so kept the locomotives in better mechanical condition. Therefore with the engines in LMSR lot 187 turned out in 1947-48 this practice was adopted as standard for new construction with both plain and roller bearings. Many older engines were converted as they went through the shops, particularly the thirty-five bronze-lined engines, which were all so equipped by July 1951.

By 1952 the average distance between a heavy repair and the next intermediate shopping of Class 5s fitted with these liners was 97,000 miles, contrasted with 57,000 miles of the original type, but some of this substantial betterment was due to improved frame staying by the link-and-pin horn cross ties of horizontal T-section, stiffer

horn blocks, and different springing put in gradually over previous years. From the beginning of 1951 these improvements were programmed for 643 of the older Class 5 engines in accordance with Table XIV; the strengthening plates around the driving horn gaps put in since 1941 to a growing number of locomotives were then removed. This programme was put into abeyance in 1958 and many Black Fives were never modified in the above respects.

The resulting better mechanical condition throughout the period between shoppings was reflected in performance and direct running costs, and observations made 1953-54 on five engines showed that a Class 5 in poor mechanical order could develop only 90 per cent of the output of one in first class order, and at a coal/dbhphr rate 8 to 13 per cent higher. Before the incorporation of the manganese-steel liners and other frame improvements the Black Fives in regard to shoppings were scarcely ahead of the mixed-traffic 4-6-0s of other Group lines, though exact comparisons were difficult because of the different work allowed to be done at depots between intermediates. The Black Fives at that time were brought in for box repairs around 57,000 miles, but sometimes went through two of these intermediates before the boiler was lifted off and a general repair given to the whole locomotive at 145,000 to 170,000 miles. With the manganese liners only one intermediate was needed between general repairs, and by 1956-57 the average between general repairs was 182,000 miles.

From the beginning Stanier, following GWR practice, had used tapered rectangular-section coupling rods though retaining I-section for the 11ft 3in connecting rods; but from 1944 I-section rods were used and came to be regarded as standard in new construction, and were kept for all further LMSR and BR construction of Black Fives. Twin brake shoes for each coupled wheel were introduced in 1938 in place of the previous 15in single block, first in the twenty Crewe-built Nos. 5452-71 for Scotland. This practice was perpetuated in the war-time and Ivatt engines.

As built, the first 472 Class 5 engines only just kept within the 1928 recommended limits of the Bridge Stress Committee in regard to hammer-blow, for in nearly all as much as two-thirds of the reciprocating weights of 933 lb/side were balanced in the wheels, and at 5 revs/sec (64mph) gave a wheel hammer-blow of 3.84 tons and an axle hammer-blow of 4.28 tons. The Committee had been concerned mainly with vertical impact forces and at the speeds then common; but by 1935 Black Fives were often attaining 75-80mph (6 revs/sec), at which speed axle hammer-blow was 6.25 tons.

Resulting from a study of American tests made in 1937-38 with comparatively small coupled wheels run up to high speeds, slipping tests were undertaken by the LMSR early in 1939, and when at a linear speed of 10-12mph slipping on oiled rails got Class 5 engine No. 5043 to an equivalent speed of 103mph (8 revs/sec) the 6ft 0in driving wheels rose 2.4in off the rails once every revolution, coming down with a corresponding thump and a *real* hammer-blow of 9.82 tons.

The percentage of reciprocating weight balanced thereupon was reduced, and though 30 and 40 per cent were tried at first these gave rise to longitudinal forces that were deemed excessive, and eventually 50 per cent was selected as the standard amount, and was applied to all new construction from 1943. The older engines were altered gradually from 1939, but engines ran for years with 40, 50, 55 or 66 per cent balance.

With 50 per cent balance the hammer-blow per axle was 3.5 tons at 64mph, 5.5 tons at 80mph, and 8.9 tons at 100mph; at 100mph wheel lift off the rail was still 0.4in every revolution, and even at 90mph some rail damage resulted, for at that speed hammer-blow was 6.6 tons/wheel, 7.8 tons/axle, 16.8 tons/rail, and 20.1 tons for the whole engine.

Left: Southbound freight near Shap quarries in charge of Caprotti No. 44749 in 1964 shortly before withdrawal. *(Derek Cross)*

Below: One of the ten sloping-throatplate steel-firebox Black Fives of 1949 on the turntable at Camden depot. *(Peter Holdstock)*

Many Class 5s operating in Scotland were equipped with tablet-catchers, and many also were provided in winter with small buffer-beam snow clearers. Hudd automatic warning apparatus was put on Nos. 4984 and 5267 from 1947 for operation over the Tilbury section. From 1958 BR aws equipment was installed gradually, and had the usual coupling protection plate in front and small cylindrical reservoirs on the running plates in front of the cab. Ash ejectors were put on Nos. 5334, 5415/35/51 in 1942-44, and from around the same period improved ashpans were applied to obviate the small clearance between damper doors and trailing axlebox guides, and the revised type also was arranged for easier raking out.

A Smith-Stone speed recorder was put on No. 44754 in 1949 as an experiment, but not until February 1961 was an extension made, beginning with Nos. 44830 and 45267; but a long-prior application had been scheduled in January 1938 for twenty engines on the Midland Division that were doing a good deal of passenger work. Not all twenty were fitted when a war-time directive of January 1940 suspended the work, and soon after the equipment fitted was removed and put into store. Proposals in 1938 had been gradually to fit speedometers to all Class 5s.

Electric lighting with Stone's turbo-generating set was put on Nos. 44658, 44755-57 and 4765-67 when new in 1947-48, but the apparatus, which included cab lights as well as head lamps, was removed in 1952-53 because of numerous small

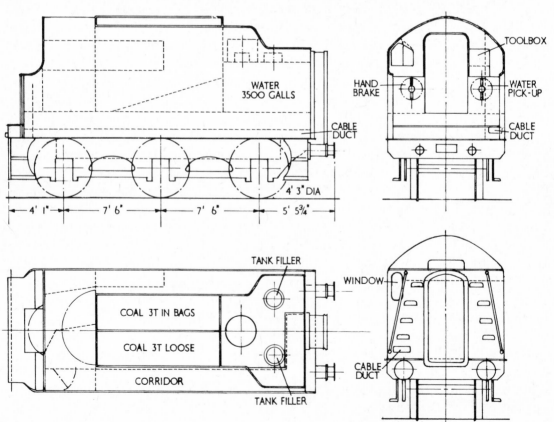

WATER
3500 GALLS

CABLE
DUCT

4' 3" DIA

4' 1"   7' 6"   7' 6"   5' 5¾"

TOOLBOX

HAND
BRAKE

WATER
PICK-UP

CABLE
DUCT

TANK FILLER

COAL 3T IN BAGS

COAL 3T LOOSE

CORRIDOR

TANK FILLER

WINDOW

CABLE
DUCT

Left: One of the four special coal-weighing tenders that ran attached to various Black Fives for test purposes. *(R. T. Ellis collection)*

Left lower: **Fig 22** Layout of special one-off corridor tender with two coal bunkers, for test runs.

defects. Initial cost per locomotive was some £300 higher with this equipment.

Steel inside fireboxes were put into Nos. 44718-27 when new, and as far as is known ran throughout the lives of these locomotives. Curiously these boxes resulted in a cost lower by only 2 per cent, £11,580 per engine and tender against £11,826 of normal copper-box engines of the same period. In 1947 Nos. 4826/7/9/30/44 were converted to oil burning, and while so equipped had a small 'x' painted on the cab sides below the number. They reverted to coal burning in 1948.

A late change, undertaken in the 1960s, was the removal of the highest lamp bracket from the top of the smokebox door, above the hand rail, to a much lower position to the right (when facing the front) of the central door fastening; this was done to lessen risk of contacting overhead wires on the growing electrified mileage when changing lamps. Prior to that, proposals to fit one of the Class 5s with a Crosti boiler had been negatived.

Original Class 5 official diagram ED177 showed a Fowler-type 3500-gallon straight-sided tender attached, but this combination was not effected, and from the beginning Stanier 4000-gallon 9-ton tenders were attached. Over the years they varied in tare weight from 26.8 to 27.9 tons, the weights in general following the tank construction, that is, riveted, welded, and a combination of both, the fully-welded pattern being the lightest. All types had handscrew-operated water pick-up, and vacuum-controlled steam brakes operated in conjunction with the locomotive equipment. An armoured hose led from one vehicle to the other, and apart from the train pipe and hose connections there was no vacuum equipment on the tender. A handscrew brake was bevel-and-shaft operated from the right-hand side. Both steam and hand brakes applied the same single block on the rear side of each 51in wheel. From locomotive Nos. 5452-71 (welded tender numbers 9708-27) water-spray pipes were fitted horizontally along the tops of the bunker sides.

To locomotive No. 5000 on its completion at Crewe in February 1935 was attached tender No. 9002 built specially with roller-bearing axle-boxes in 1933 for the Royal Scot locomotive that went on the North American tour. On its return in 1934 this tender was rebuilt to the new high-sided curved-top pattern, as were tenders Nos. 9000-01 taken from the first two Stanier Pacifics Nos. 6200-01 and attached to Black Fives Nos. 5073-74.

Of the other nineteen Crewe-built engines of the first order, Nos. 5001-17 took the tenders intended originally for Nos. 5000-10 and 5013-18 in sequence, and Nos. 5018-19 were provided with tenders 9164-65 intended for locomotives Nos. 5070-71. Engine Nos. 5070-72 took the tenders due for Nos. 5072-74. Tenders for the first twenty Crewe-built locomotives were not included in the Crewe order 377, but were constructed under a separate order T390. In the meantime the first fifty VF locomotives Nos. 5020-69 were delivered with Vulcan-built tenders that were given LMSR tender numbers 9074-9123.

The fifty-five locomotives of 1935, Nos. 5070-5124, were given the straight tender number sequence 9166-9218 with the exception of engines Nos. 5073-74 which had the rebuilt tenders numbers 9000-01, as mentioned earlier. Through 1947-50 the three tenders 9000-02 were modified by the provision of manganese-steel liners to the axleboxes, plus an improved method of registering the journals and special ventilation to overcome corrosion in the boxes. Tender numbers for all locomotive deliveries are included in Table X.

The original allotment to locomotive No. 5019 (tender 9073) appears to be the vehicle completed as a special test-train tender, which was given a corridor down the left-hand side and a vestibule connection at the back. This special tender bore number 4999; it was begun at Crewe to order X3/285 and completed at Derby under order 0-1228. In the LMSR tender list number 9073 remained blank. The coal bunker was divided longitudinally; in one half was three tons of coal and in the other half three tons in weighed bags. The appearance is shown in Fig. 22. Though built more-or-less in the Black Five tender sequence it was painted LMSR red. It ran attached to various locomotives under test, but eventually was rebuilt with a standard body, though retaining its distinctive number, and finished its days attached to Class 5 No. 45235 through 1965-66.

For all the contract-built engines and for almost every other Black Five after 1935 the tenders fitted initially were in correct number sequence; only in much later orders did variations come when four special coal-weighing tenders were attached to other than the intended locomotives. These tenders were Nos. 10590-91 built in 1946 and Nos. 10836-37 in 1950-51. The former pair had a coal capacity of 8 tons and the last two 8½ tons. They were attached nominally in number sequence to locomotives Nos. 4986, 4966, 44696 and 44677. Actually No. 10590 had been meant for engine 4965, but an exchange was made with that for 4986. The final batch of forty Black Five tenders was attached in correct order except that Nos. 44677 and 44697 exchanged allotted tenders. Changes of tender within Class 5 were made at times, but a high proportion of the 842 engines seems to have kept the same tenders for life.

The reason for the four coal-weighing tenders lay in the rising cost of coal and deterioration in quality; the intention was to check consumptions and the effects of different sources of coal supply on day-to-day working, by monitoring methods of firing. The tender design was prepared in conjunction with Transport & General Engineering (Leeds) Ltd. The standard frame and wheels of the 4000-gallon Stanier tender were used, but the body was modified so that the self-trimming bunker was set on shafts attached by levers to a steelyard at the back of the bunker. Normally the bunker was locked so that the weight was carried on brackets attached to the body, avoiding vibration and damage to the weighing gear. When weighing was required the locks were released and the bunker weight taken by the shafts running on either side and transmitted to the weighing levers and steelyard. Weighing was done only with the locomotive stationary. In practice little use seems to have been made of these weighing facilities. Indeed, in October 1949, nine tenders were scheduled for construction by BR, but only two were built.

Of the tenders allotted to Class 5 locomotives, Nos. 9002, 9054-64, 9067-72, 9074-9123, 9164-65, and 9166-9218 had tanks of riveted construction. All 327 AW locomotives (Nos. 5125-5451) had welded tender tanks, and possibly this construction was due to AW suggestions. Welded tenders were attached also to Nos. 5452-71 of 1938 and to Nos. 5472-99 and 4800-06 of 1943-44. Beginning with No. 4807 in 1944, tender tanks were of combined welded and riveted fabrication, and in official lists bore the same Mark I as the earlier fully-riveted tenders, whereas the welded type was known as Mark II.

To match up with the thirty Ivatt locomotives given roller-bearing axleboxes, the attached tenders also were so fitted. These were Nos. 10640-49 (attached to locomotives 44758-67), 10650-59 (locomotives 44748-57), and 10818-27 (locomotives 44678-87). These could be distinguished by the circular axlebox covers; the standard plain-bearing box covers were rectangular. The only Class 5 known to have had any other type of tender was No. 45329 which ran in 1964-65 with a type (c) 3500-gallon curved top unit, but this was noted by few observers.

Until repaintings after the beginning of World War II the engines and tenders were painted black with a single red lining to boiler, firebox, cab sides, running angle and cylinder cleading. VF-built engines also had a single red line round the cab windows. Buffer beams were red with a 1-in black border. 12in gold leaf numerals were put on the cab sides and above them were the 3in numerals and letters of the power classification; but in Nos. 5452-71 of 1938 the colour of the insignia was the then new standard yellow.

The first 225 engines had shaded scroll and serif numerals and letters, as had Nos. 5452-71, but the 227 locomotives delivered by AW in 1936-37 had the then new sans numerals and letters with red shading, and this form was extended to the cast-iron number plates on the smokebox doors. With Nos. 5452-71 of 1938 the reversion to scroll and serif form took effect. The majority, if not all, of the first 225 engines had the 15in tender letters *LMS* grouped closer together than the standard 5ft 0in spacing. From resumption of Class 5 construction in 1943 all new engines were delivered in plain unlined black with unshaded yellow lettering and numerals, and the buffer beams also were black. This style was applied also to repaints.

From 1947 the lined straw-coloured insignia were applied with sans lettering and numerals, though not many Class 5s got them barring the twenty new engines, Nos. 4997-99, 4783-89, 4700-09 completed at Horwich in 1947, and Crewe-built engines Nos. 4748-52 and 4758-68. Though with sans insignia, these engines had scroll and script figures on the smokebox plates.

After the formation of BR, that organisation's black colour and standard lining and lettering was adopted, though not until 1957 were all

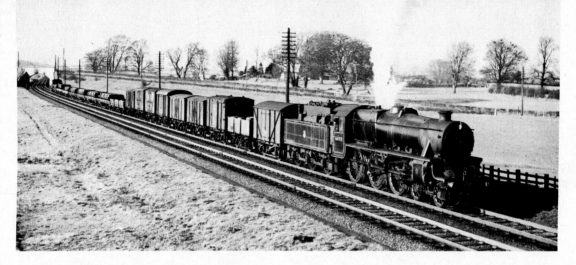

Above: No. 44971 with coal-weighing tender attached on an up through freight at Holme on the old Lancaster & Carlisle main line in 1955. *(Ian S. Pearsall)*

Below: AW sloping-throatplate domed-boiler Class 5 of 1936, as running in 1948 in unlined black. Still with original left-hand crosshead with bolting face for vacuum pump eight years after removal of the latter.

Class 5s lined-out instead of being plain black, while No. 45493 repainted in September of that year is thought to have been the last to get the BR standard livery. From late 1963 lining was omitted from repaints.

In 1948 experimental liveries were applied to individual Class 5s preceding the final choice of BR colour. No. 4762 was Southern green, 4763 LNER green, and 4764 GWR green. At the same time No. 45225 was painted lined-black for comparison, which scheme was chosen. The tenders of all four were lettered BRITISH RAILWAYS.

In the early days of BR many engines were given the prefix M to denote London Midland Region. Class 5 engines carrying the M were Nos. 4748-54/62-64, 4820/40/1/62,

5012/8/48/64/77/81/9/99, 5101/13/4/7/27/61/5, 5253/92, 5352/9/69/74, 5407/59/76. The M was put above the numeral, and the 5 of the power classification transferred below; an M prefix was found also on the smokebox number plate. Northern (Scottish) Division engines in LMSR days often had smaller insignia than normal; in BR days they had larger than standard, and usually had 5MT in place of the simple 5.

Only five engines (see foot of Table XVI end of this chapter) received names in LMSR days, and these were confined to Scottish yeomanry and territorial regiments. Nos. 5157-58 were named in 1936 while shedded at St. Rollox, and two more received names in 1936-37. Below the name was the badge of the regiment and a detail

of the unit. No. 5155 was named *Queens Edinburgh* (*sic*) in December 1942 but bore the name only until 1944. In that year a check had to be made of several LMSR engines as to just what names they did carry, and No. 5155 was one of those 'checked in shed'.

Works plates on the first fifty Vulcans and on some at least of the first 100 Armstrongs were attached to the smokebox sides; those of the 227 AW engines were secured to the front ends of the frame plates, and this position was adopted for the second fifty from VF and for all engines from LMSR works. Frame attachment of the works plates did not bring any continuity in the identity of an engine, for from 1943 a spare set of frames was available, and a general policy of changing round boilers and frames to get a quick return to traffic from Crewe repair shops led to few 27ft 2in wheelbase locomotives remaining intact throughout their lives.

During 1937 trials were made with Class 5s between London and Manchester over the Midland route. The two engines involved, Nos. 5264 and 5278, both AW build with sloping-throatplate boilers and 24-element superheaters, were given an eight-car train of 258 tons, including dynamometer car, and ran the 190 miles in charge of one crew in times of 195½ minutes southbound and 202 minutes northbound. Coal consumption averaged 6450 lb and water consumption 4825 gallons for the 190 miles. Southbound the 99 miles from Leicester to London were covered start-to-stop in 92.5 minutes with top speeds of 85, 87 and 91mph (6.6 to 7.1 revs/sec) at different points, but the effects on the rails of the hammer-blows of 22.2 tons/rail and 26.5 tons for the whole locomotive (then with two-thirds reciprocating balance) were not recorded.

On the basis of these tests and some other observations, Stanier gave figures in 1938 showing economical dbhp as peaking around 950 at 30mph and being above 900 from 20 to 45mph; he gave ihp as 1080 maximum at 45mph. These figures were deliberately conservative, for uphill to Peak Forest in the

1937 tests the engines developed 1300 or more ihp and produced an equivalent dbhp of well over 1100, and further south a peak above 1000dbhp was attained up 1 in 130 at 55-60mph. These curves of Stanier's are given in Fig. 23, and above them have been added values actually attained in service or on Rugby test plant.

More trials were conducted in 1939 between London and Leeds on express passenger trains and between Sheffield and Carlisle on fitted freights, to test maximum traffic capacities and to relate schedules to fuel consumption. On the London-Leeds route a check was made of the relative efficiencies and consumptions of 14-element and 21-element superheater engines.

Northbound the fitted freight was of forty-five wagons totalling 562 tons trailing including dynamometer car; southbound a fifty-wagon train of 610 tons was hauled over the 150 miles. Over the return freight trip the averages were 55.7lb coal/mile, 3.13lb coal/dbhphr, 41.5 gal water/mile, 23.3lb water/dbhphr, and 7.44lb water/lb coal evaporation rate. On the northbound trip the 1 in 100 ascent to Blea Moor involved 40-45 per cent cut-off and full regulator; elsewhere cut-off rarely rose above 35-37 per cent. Southbound 30 to 35 per cent cut-off sufficed from Carlisle to Appleby and 45 to 60 per cent on the succeeding 1 in 100 to Ais Gill, both with full throttle.

On the passenger turns train weight was 300-310 tons including dynamometer car, and scheduled running speeds were 50-52mph for the 196 miles. Cut-offs of 23 to 28 per cent were sufficient except southbound from Sheffield to Dore & Totley, over which stretch 35 per cent was used. With the 21-element engine No. 5079 average consumptions were 43.7lb coal/mile, 3.23lb coal/dbhphr, 32.8 gal water/mile, 24.3lb water/dbhphr, 63.6lb coal/sfg/hr/firing rate, and 7.49lb unit evaporation rate. The

14-element superheater locomotive No. 5067 also with vertical-throatplate boiler showed 49.5lb coal/mile, 3.97lb coal/dbhphr, 38.2 gal water/mile, 30.6lb water/dbhphr, 74lb coal/sfg/hr firing rate, and 7.72 lb unit evaporation rate. No. 5067 had run 20,600 miles since its last general repair, while No. 5079 had done 4620 miles. Final steam temperature with the 21-element engine averaged 80°F more than with the 14-element type.

In 1949 line tests were made partly to run in and gain experience with the then new LMR 60ft 40-ton No. 3 dynamometer car and associated mobile testing units (which had been put in hand during Stanier's time), the latter simulating a counter-pressure braking locomotive by electrical means. First No. 45372 ran briefly with these vehicles on the Rugby-Peterborough line, then in September, after a few runs between Derby and Leicester, a six-day series of tests was made with No. 44764 between Rugby and Willesden in each direction, in which constant-speed tests, each of 30 to 60 minutes' duration, were effected at 10, 20, 30, 40, 50 and 60mph. One of the special coal-weighing tenders was attached. At 40 per cent cut-off and 40mph with a drawbar pull of 12,350lb, equal to 1300dbhp, water consumption was only 17lb/dbhphr, and this was the minimum achieved. Speed-load curves drawn up from these tests gave 1200 tons at 30mph along the level and 500 tons up 1 in

Top left: Black Five of 1950 built with Walschaerts motion, piston valves, and SKF roller-bearing axleboxes throughout engine and tender. BR red-lined black livery with the first BR emblem on the tender. *(J. B. Radford collection)*

Right: **Fig 23** Curves of Black Five indicated and drawbar horsepowers.

Left: One of the five named Black Fives, *Glasgow Yeomanry,* as it appeared when named in 1936. It ran with these nameplates until withdrawal in 1964.

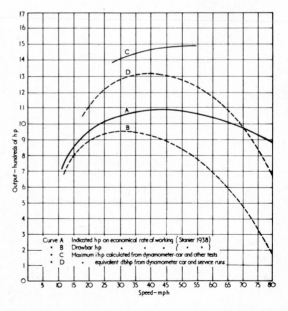

Curve A Indicated hp on economical rate of working (Stanier 1938)
" B Drawbar hp . . . . (" ")
" C Maximum ihp calculated from dynamometer car and other tests
" D equivalent dbhp from dynamometer car and service runs

100 at 20mph as practical values for the operating department.

During June to October 1950 blastpipe and chimney experiments were conducted at Rugby test plant with No. 44764 (Timken bearings and Walschaerts motion) and general tests carried out. On the plant continuous output as limited by the boiler was 1160dbhp at 37-38mph and 920dbhp at 60mph. On a shorter time basis 1320dbhp at 40mph was attained with 40 per cent cut-off and an actual boiler pressure of 210lb/sq in; with 30 per cent cut-off 7200lb drawbar pull at 60mph (or 1150dbhp) was reached, and about 690dbhp was still available at 80mph.

Some improvement was made in evaporation by reducing the taper inside the chimney from the standard 1 in 7 to 1 in 14, and increasing the distance between chimney top and choke from 24.4 in to 28in, retaining the standard 5⅛in blast nozzle; for given cut-offs this increased the draught by some 10 per cent. This chimney alteration formed the basis of the BR Class 5MT drafting arrangements.

Later in 1950 clean and dirty boiler tests were undertaken at Rugby with No. 44862, and further plant tests were made with No. 45218 with various piston-valve heads to give small changes in lead, but as no corresponding changes in lap or valve motion proportions were made they had limited effect. Nevertheless they showed optimum lead was important, a feature well borne out in practice, where incorrect lead could produce a rough-running engine with decided axlebox knock and fore-and-aft vibration and where, whatever the lead, linking-up to 15-18 per cent led to pounding and surging, and to wear and knock in the trailing boxes. Basically these results could well have been due to the 6:1 ratio of lap to lead, a value that did not promote successful linking-up below some 20 per cent.

In January 1952 some trials were conducted with No. 3 dynamometer car and fifty-two laden coal wagons double-headed by Nos. 45342 and 44667 on Midland Division mineral trains between Toton and Brent (Hendon), a service which in its time had seen Midland single-drivers and several classes of 0-6-0, Tilbury 4-6-4Ts, Midland 0-6-4Ts, and on one occasion 'Big Bertha', the Lickey 0-10-0 banker, and which was later to see the BR Crosti-boiler 2-10-0s.

Highest output recorded by a Class 5 during the 1948 Interchange Trials (No. 45253 of 1936 AW build) was 1283 equivalent dbhp at 40 per cent cut-off, full throttle and 213psi actual boiler pressure when taking a 440-ton train at 50.5mph up the 1 in 174 preceding the steepest part of Wellington bank on the Western Region main line; 1240 equivalent dbhp was exerted up the 1 in 36 of Dainton bank at 27mph with 45 per cent cut-off and 275 tons trailing. These were in the course of the 127-mile through run between Bristol and Plymouth, over which coal consumption averaged 38lb/mile southbound and 45lb/mile northbound.

On the ex-Great Central section the engine attained 1000dbhp and about 1225edbhp at 45 per cent cut-off at 34.6mph up 1 in 117 between Dinting and Woodhead. On the Highland section, with 440 tons trailing, No. 44799 did not reach such high figures despite the long 1 in 60 to 1 in 100 grades, and little exceeded 900 actual dbhp and 1130edbhp up 1 in 95 at 32mph and 37 per cent cut-off. Up 1 in 60 at 24mph and 40 per cent cut-off the output was 730dbhp and 1000edbhp, a low-speed output exceeded substantially by No. 5079 on the pre-war Sheffield-Carlisle freight trials with 21,250lb drawbar pull at 17.2mph with 60 per cent cut-off, equal to 975dbhp.

Average evaporation rate of the Class 5s during the 1948 Interchange Trials on Western, Eastern, Scottish and London Midland Regions was 7.92lb water/lb coal; on a power basis the averages were 3.54lb coal/dbhphr and 28lb water/dbhphr. Per mile the average coal consumption was 41.5lb. Strangely, the two Class 5 engines involved scarcely maintained the normal daily LMSR performances.

The first Black Five delivered, No. 5020, was retained at Crewe for testing, and worked for some time on the Western Division main line, where it achieved, inter alia, the feat of ascending the south side of Tring with the 2.40pm Euston-Liverpool loading to fifteen vehicles (including dynamometer car) of 480/490 tons trailing at a minimum of 54mph, equal to about 1460 rail hp, and going up to Whitmore at 60mph minimum, approximating to 1200dbhp and around 1650 rail hp—standards of performance never bettered in later years.

The next nine engines from VF, Nos. 5021-29, were sent to Perth and the Highland section, and at once revolutionised possibilities over the Perth-Inverness line, and they could run over the old route via Forres from which the Horwich Crabs were debarred by their maximum axle load of 19.6 tons, though their loading per foot run of engine wheelbase was no greater than that of the Black Fives. On this main line they double-headed trains of 500-520 tons without further banking assistance up the 1 in 60-70 grades. By February 1935 the new 4-6-0s were being used also north of Inverness as far as Wick. Not until November 1938 were they permitted over the ex-Caledonian line to Oban, and it was one of the AW 5350 series that was derailed in the Pass of Brander by fallen boulders on 8 August 1946. By 1939 Inverness had twenty Black Fives working over most Highland routes, but the thirty-two additional engines at Perth worked on diagrams that took them to Crewe, Glasgow, Aberdeen and Wick.

Some of the succeeding VF engines were put on the Glasgow-Aberdeen services with a daily mileage above 300 per locomotive, and others went to the former Midland Railway Birmingham-Bristol line, but for some three years were not allowed over the Mangotsfield-Bath offshoot. As more were delivered their use spread to other parts of the Midland Division south of Manchester and Leeds. Speeds up to 80mph were reached from the beginning, and 90mph topped on the trials of 1937. The large deliveries through 1935 permitted withdrawal of many ex-LNWR Prince of Wales and 19in goods 4-6-0s; indeed Nos. 5125-5224 were ordered specifically to replace 108 of the latter.

After the Mangotsfield-Bath bridges had been strengthened Class 5s could go south over the Somerset & Dorset line, and No. 5432 was the first to travel over the route, with the 10.20am ex-Bath on 2 May 1938. From that date the Black Fives were to be seen almost over the limits of LMSR locomotive working, from Bournemouth in the south to Wick in the north, and from Holyhead in the west and Swansea in the south west to Hull in the east; certain lines such as those to Stranraer and Keswick had to wait until 1939 for the installation of the necessary 60ft turntables. Because of curtailment in through passenger services from the north, Class 5 engines were almost withdrawn from the Somerset & Dorset line from early in the war until the end of 1944.

On the formation of BR on 1 January 1948 the LMSR handed over 742 Black Fives. They were allocated: 335 on the Western Division, 97 on the Central Division, 104 on the Midland Division, and 206 on the Northern (Scottish) Division. For heavy repairs 536 were allocated to Crewe and the 206 Scottish engines to St Rollox.

During BR time the working widened considerably, but until regional boundary changes in 1957 only a few at Bath West (SR) and Shrewsbury (WR) were not at LMR or ScR sheds, though in the latter region there was some running over ex-LNER lines, notably over the West Highland route to Fort William. Largest groups of these engines were at Willesden, Rugby, Aston, Crewe North and South, Edge Hill, Longsight, Patricroft, Carnforth, Carlisle Upperby, Kentish Town, Derby, Leeds, Saltley, Blackpool, Newton Heath, Carlisle Kingmoor, St Rollox, Perth and Inverness. Perth in 1954 had the almost incredible number of sixty-five allocated. Average annual mileages of the LMR and ScR engines in BR days are given in Table XV.

The first transfer away from the LMR lines took place in an emergency in June 1953, when Nos. 45051/61, 45130, 45216/22/3 and 45350 went to the SR on the temporary total

TABLE XV BLACK FIVE PERFORMANCE IN BR DAYS (1)

Year	LM Region (3)		Scottish Region (3)		Nos 44738–47 (4)		Nos 44748–57 (4)		No 44767 (5)	
	Mileage	Availa-bility %	Mileage	Availa-bility %	Mileage	Availa-bility %	Mileage	Availa-bility %	Mileage	Availa-bility %
1951	38,530	82	43,397	76	37,697	82	46,717	78	59,278	86
1952	39,826	81	42,473	76	42,715	80	43,796	72	51,629	65
1953	40,289	81	44,594	76	40,273	74	48,048	81	56,409	79
1954	40,221	82	44,930	78	44,180	78	43,860	78	54,430	71
1955	38,511	79	43,183	76	36,975	70	40,365	71	53,065	75
1956	40,626	81	42,663	76	45,004	81	42,718	74	46,453	68
1957	40,566	82	43,663	76	41,793	76	45,142	85	57,751	81
1958	39,428	79	40,614	74	38,882	77	47,656	89	44,928	71
1959	39,427	(2)	41,630	(2)	41,495	(2)	38,869	(2)	47,140	(2)
1960	37,138	(2)	37,928	(2)	35,495	(2)	37,610	(2)	51,780	(2)
1961	37,129	(2)	32,728	(2)	33,203	(2)	25,689	(2)	47,098	(2)

(1) Mileage given is average/loco/year; (2) Availability recording discontinued; (3) Figures for standard locomotives allocated to region; (4) Caprotti valve gear; (5) Stephenson link motion.

withdrawal of the Merchant Navy Pacifics due to axle troubles; before transfer of the seven engines could be made the footsteps had to be moved in an inch or two, the injector overflow pipes cut back, and the SR range of lamp brackets provided.

The regional changes in 1957 also took Class 5s at some Yorkshire depots into the Eastern Region (Sheffield area) and North Eastern Region (Leeds area), but the general sphere of working was not greatly altered until about 1961, from which time they worked beyond Hereford and Gloucester into South Wales, beyond Bristol to the south, and over SR lines on through trains. On the Midland Division they shared some of the Leicester-London accelerated workings of 1957-58 with the Jubilees, and were timed at 88-90mph on occasions with 260/275-ton trains, performances good for neither locomotive nor track.

Quite a number of Royal trains were handled by Black Fives in BR days, generally with double-heading, including the special from St Pancras to Barrow via Leeds and Skipton on 10 August 1956 with Nos. 45285 and 45279; another along the Midland main line on 26 March 1956 was worked by No. 45285 solo on a train of LNER Royal stock, while there was the remarkable use of Nos. 45332, 45236, 45197, 45037, 45246 and 45449 in succession on a five-coach train for Prince Philip over the West Cumberland lines on 22-24 November 1955. No. 45278, also in spotless condition, was used in 1956 for the filming of J. B. Priestley's *The Good Companions*.

Black Fives figured in three major accidents. First, on 13 October 1939. No. 5025 piloting Royal Scot No. 6130 on the 7.50pm Euston-Stranraer train, after passing six adverse signals in two miles ran into the 7.37pm Euston-Inverness train in Bletchley station while an ex-LNWR 0-8-0 No. 9169 was shunting a four-wheel van on to the back of that train. The passed fireman driving No. 5025 was tried for manslaughter but acquitted. The second was at Lichfield on 1 January 1946 when No. 5495 at the head of a fish train was turned by mischance from the up fast line into the occupied platform line, while in the third, at Sutton Coldfield on 23 January 1953, No. 45274 hauling the 12.15pm (Sunday) York-Bristol train left the track through excessive speed over a restricted length. Though badly damaged it was repaired and continued in stock until 1967. At the time of the

accident No. 45274 had covered 747,517 miles since completion in 1936, and 105,283 miles since its last general repair, but it had been given an intermediate repair the preceding August, after which it had run about 25,000 miles. Details of the work that could be done at an 'intermediate' in those days are interesting. According to the official accident report, in August 1952 the engine had been given new cylinders, new tyres, and new axlebox bearing brasses; the horn surfaces had been re-metalled and a frame crack welded. The engine had not then acquired manganese-steel liners to the horns.

The first withdrawal of a Black Five was that of No. 45401 in November 1961 following a collision with Jubilee No. 45630 at Warrington some three months earlier. Regular withdrawal began in 1962 and all were gone by the end of 1968, the rate of withdrawal being twenty-one in 1962, twenty-nine in 1963, sixty-seven in 1964, ninety-seven in 1965, 171 in 1966, 305 in 1967, and 151 in 1968. Withdrawal dates of all are recorded in Table XVI. No effort was made to pull out of service early the small-grate vertical-throatplate engines of 1934-35, over thirty of which continued until 1968. The twenty Caprotti locomotives of 1947-48 went in 1963-65, except No. 44743 which lasted until 1966; even the two improved Caprotti locomotives of 1951 disappeared in 1965-66.

The final survivors were all concentrated in Lancashire during the last few months of steam in 1968. The last standard-gauge ordinary timetabled trains of BR to be steam-hauled were the 8.50pm Preston to Blackpool (No. 45212) and the 9.25pm Preston-Liverpool Exchange (No. 45318) on Saturday 3 August; the last ordinary fare-paying passengers to be moved by steam were those in the sleeping cars of the 11.45pm from Euston to Preston, when the coaches were stabled in the early hours of the Sunday by No. 45212. On the so-called final day of steam staged on 11 August 1968 by BR, three Class 5s partook in the working of the special from Liverpool and Manchester to Carlisle and back—No. 45110 from Liverpool to Manchester and back, with Nos. 44781 and 44871 on the return from Carlisle to Manchester.

At the moment of writing (August 1976) thirteen Black Fives are preserved and a few more may remain in parlous state in Welsh scrapyards eight years after withdrawal. The preserved engines are: 44767 (now on the North

No. 5025, by then provided with a dome to the original domeless boiler, involved in the collision with ex-LNWR 0-8-0 No. 9169 and the night Euston-Inverness train in Bletchley station, 13 October 1939. The 0-8-0 was pushed over the frame of a van it was attaching to the Inverness train, and its tender mounted the platform.

Yorkshire Moors Railway after some years at Steamtown, Carnforth); 44806 (Lakeside, and owned by Mr Kenneth Aldcroft); 44871 (Steamtown); 44932 (Steamtown); 45000 (now at the National Railway Museum, York, after years in store at Preston Park, Brighton); 45025 (now on the Strathspey Railway at Aviemore, after some years on the Keighley & Worth Valley Railway); 45110 (Severn Valley Railway); 45212 (Keighley & Worth Valley); 45231 (Main Line Steam Trust, Loughborough); 45305 (owned by Alfred Draper & Son Ltd, Hull); 45379 (Bristol Suburban Railway, Bitton); 45407 (Steamtown); and 45428 (Standard-Gauge Steam Trust, Tyseley, and now on the North Yorkshire Moors Railway).

Some of these preserved engines have reverted to their LMSR numbers. Since acquisition by the present owners No. 45110 was named *RAF Biggin Hill* in 1970, and No. 45428 *Eric Treacy* in 1969. After withdrawal, the Stephenson-motion engine No. 44767 was named *Cecil J. Allen*, but in August 1975 was renamed *George Stephenson*, and below the nameplates on the front splashers are plaques reading: 'This locomotive was named by the Rt Hon William Whitelaw, CH, MC, MP, at Shildon on August 25th 1975 to commemorate the 150th Anniversary of the Stockton & Darlington Railway'. This engine was in the Grand Steam Cavalcade at Shildon on 31 August 1975. At the moment of writing proposals are to name No. 45231 *3rd (Volunteer) Battalion The Worcestershire and Sherwood Foresters Regiment*, probably the longest name ever given to a British locomotive.

TABLE XVI STANIER CLASS 5 MIXED TRAFFIC 4—6—0 LOCOMOTIVES, LMSR/BR

First No	Date into t'fic	Date BR No	With-drawn	First No	Date into t'fic	Date BR No	With-drawn	First No	Date into t'fic	Date BR No	With-drawn
44658*	5/49	New	11/67	44679	5/50	New	9/67	44700	7/48	New	7/66
44659	5/49	New	6/67	44680	6/50	New	9/67	44701	8/48	New	6/64
44660	5/49	New	8/64	44681	6/50	New	9/67	44702	8/48	New	6/65
44661	6/49	New	8/67	44682	6/50	New	11/67	44703	8/48	New	12/66
44662	6/49	New	9/67	44683	7/50	New	4/68	44704	9/48	New	9/66
44663	6/49	New	5/68	44684	7/50	New	9/67	44705	9/48	New	9/66
44664	6/49	New	5/68	44685	8/50	New	4/67	44706	9/48	New	12/63
44665	6/49	New	3/68	44686*	4/51	New	10/65	44707	9/48	New	1/66
44666	7/49	New	2/67	44687*	5/51	New	1/66	44708	10/48	New	1/68
44667	7/49	New	9/67	44688	8/50	New	8/66	44709	10/48	New	8/68
44668	12/49	New	4/66	44689	9/50	New	3/67	44710	10/48	New	12/66
44669	12/49	New	10/67	44690	10/50	New	8/68	44711	10/48	New	5/68
44670	1/50	New	1/66	44691	10/50	New	3/67	44712	10/48	New	11/66
44671	2/50	New	2/67	44692	10/50	New	5/66	44713	11/48	New	8/68
44672	2/50	New	3/68	44693	11/50	New	5/67	44714	11/48	New	11/66
44673	2/50	New	5/65	44694	12/50	New	9/67	44715	11/48	New	1/68
44674	3/50	New	12/67	44695	12/50	New	6/67	44716	11/48	New	7/65
44675	3/50	New	9/67	44696	12/50	New	5/67	44717	12/48	New	8/67
44676	4/50	New	7/64	44697	12/50	New	11/67	44718*	3/49	New	11/66
44677	4/50	New	10/67	44698	7/48	New	7/66	44719*	3/49	New	10/64
44678	5/50	New	11/67	44699	7/48	New	5/67	44720*	3/49	New	10/66

First No	Date into t'fic	Date BR No	With-drawn	First No	Date into t'fic	Date BR No	With-drawn	First No	Date into t'fic	Date BR No	With-drawn
44721*	3/49	New	8/65	4791	6/47	2/49	11/66	4861	1/45	6/48	11/67
44722*	4/49	New	4/67	4792	7/47	10/49	9/67	4862	1/45	11/49	7/67
44723*	4/49	New	10/66	4793	8/47	11/48	12/64	4863	1/45	6/49	5/67
44724*	4/49	New	10/66	4794	8/47	11/49	4/67	4864	1/45	8/48	5/68
44725*	4/49	New	10/67	4795	8/47	4/48	7/67	4865	2/45	4/49	9/67
44726*	5/49	New	10/66	4796	9/47	3/50	5/67	4866	2/45	6/48	9/67
44727*	5/49	New	10/67	4797	9/47	12/48	9/66	4867	2/45	4/48	6/67
44728	1/49	New	1/68	4798	10/47	9/49	9/66	4868	2/45	1/49	5/68
44729	1/49	New	10/66	4799	10/47	5/48	7/65	4869	3/45	8/49	9/66
44730	1/49	New	11/67	4800	5/44	11/48	3/68	4870	3/45	4/48	6/67
44731	2/49	New	4/66	4801	5/44	5/49	6/64	4871	3/45	12/49	8/68
44732	2/49	New	7/67	4802	6/44	3/49	6/68	4872	3/45	3/49	9/67
44733	2/49	New	6/67	4803	6/44	12/48	5/68	4873	3/45	12/49	11/67
44734	2/49	New	12/67	4804	6/44	11/48	3/68	4874	4/45	10/48	8/68
44735	2/49	New	8/68	4805	6/44	7/48	9/67	4875	4/45	9/48	5/67
44736	3/49	New	9/67	4806	7/44	6/49	8/68	4876	4/45	2/49	11/67
44737	3/49	New	1/67	4807	9/44	7/49	3/68	4877	4/45	7/48	8/68
44738*	6/48	New	6/64	4808	9/44	8/48	12/66	4878	5/45	9/48	7/68
44739*	6/48	New	1/65	4809	9/44	6/48	8/68	4879	5/45	8/49	4/67
44740*	5/48	New	4/63	4810	10/44	2/49	8/66	4880	5/45	6/48	11/66
44741*	6/48	New	3/65	4811	10/44	6/48	10/66	4881	5/45	8/49	7/66
44742*	6/48	New	4/64	4812	10/44	10/48	9/67	4882	6/45	6/49	7/67
44743*	6/48	New	1/66	4813	10/44	9/48	8/66	4883	6/45	2/49	7/67
44744*	7/48	New	11/63	4814	10/44	8/48	9/67	4884	6/45	1/49	6/68
44745*	7/48	New	10/64	4815	11/44	10/48	2/68	4885	7/45	6/49	12/63
44746*	8/48	New	1/64	4816	11/44	8/49	7/68	4886	7/45	7/49	10/67
44747*	7/48	New	5/63	4817	11/44	6/48	8/67	4887	8/45	12/48	12/67
M4748*	2/48	6/48	9/64	4818	11/44	10/48	6/68	4888	8/45	2/49	8/68
M4749*	2/48	6/48	9/64	4819	11/44	4/49	12/67	4889	8/45	6/49	1/68
M4750*	2/48	6/49	8/63	4820	12/44	2/50	12/66	4890	8/45	2/49	6/68
M4751*	3/48	3/49	10/64	4821	12/44	8/49	6/67	4891	8/45	3/49	6/68
M4752*	3/48	1/49	4/64	4822	12/44	5/48	10/67	4892	9/45	5/48	4/67
M4753*	3/48	6/48	7/65	4823	12/44	2/49	11/65	4893	9/45	12/48	11/67
44754*	4/48	New	4/64	4824	12/44	11/49	9/67	4894	9/45	5/49	8/68
44755*	4/48	New	11/63	4825	12/44	8/48	10/67	4895	9/45	8/49	12/67
44756*	6/48	New	10/64	4826	7/44	6/48	9/67	4896	9/45	2/49	9/67
44757*	12/48	New	11/65	4827	7/44	8/48	6/65	4897	9/45	4/49	8/68
4758*	9/47	5/48	7/68	4828	7/44	9/48	9/67	4898	9/45	1/49	10/67
4759*	9/47	3/50	11/67	4829	8/44	10/48	5/68	4899	9/45	8/49	7/68
4760*	9/47	3/50	10/66	4830	8/44	9/48	8/67	4900	10/45	7/48	6/67
4761*	10/47	3/50	4/68	4831	8/44	8/49	12/67	4901	10/45	2/50	8/65
4762*	10/47	7/49	11/66	4832	8/44	8/48	11/67	4902	10/45	5/49	11/67
4763*	10/47	8/49	9/65	4833	8/44	4/48	9/67	4903	10/45	2/49	4/68
4764*	11/47	4/49	9/65	4834	8/44	6/48	9/67	4904	10/45	11/48	12/65
4765*	12/47	9/48	9/67	4835	9/44	2/50	7/67	4905	10/45	3/50	11/67
4766*	12/47	5/48	8/67	4836	9/44	10/49	5/68	4906	10/45	4/48	3/68
4767*	12/47	4/48	12/67	4837	9/44	8/48	9/67	4907	11/45	8/49	11/67
4768	4/47	11/48	5/67	4838	9/44	8/48	3/68	4908	11/45	1/49	6/66
4769	4/47	7/48	6/65	4839	9/44	4/48	12/66	4909	11/45	8/49	9/67
4770	4/47	10/48	11/67	4840	10/44	11/50	11/67	4910	11/45	8/48	6/68
4771	5/47	12/48	3/67	4841	10/44	4/50	10/66	4911	11/45	4/49	11/67
4772	5/47	10/48	11/67	4842	10/44	8/49	1/68	4912	11/45	11/48	9/67
4773	5/47	6/48	12/67	4843	10/44	1/49	9/67	4913	11/45	2/50	7/67
4774	5/47	5/59	8/67	4844	10/44	4/48	11/67	4914	12/45	6/48	8/67
4775	6/47	3/49	11/67	4845	10/44	5/48	6/68	4915	12/45	12/49	12/67
4776	6/47	6/49	10/67	4846	11/44	5/48	1/68	4916	12/45	9/48	12/67
4777	6/47	2/49	6/68	4847	11/44	6/49	11/66	4917	12/45	1/49	11/67
4778	6/47	7/49	11/67	4848	11/44	3/49	2/68	4918	12/45	12/48	1/67
4779	7/47	4/49	12/66	4849	11/44	4/48	12/64	4919	12/45	8/48	12/66
4780	7/47	9/49	6/68	4850	11/44	6/49	7/66	4920	12/45	12/49	11/67
4781	8/47	4/49	8/68	4851	11/44	12/48	3/68	4921	1/46	9/48	2/65
4782	8/47	2/49	12/66	4852	11/44	8/49	9/67	4922	1/46	1/50	6/64
4783	3/47	6/49	6/64	4853	12/44	5/49	6/67	4923	1/46	5/50	6/64
4784	4/47	7/49	5/64	4854	12/44	8/49	9/67	4924	2/46	3/49	7/65
4785	4/47	8/49	6/64	4855	12/44	8/48	5/68	4925	2/46	2/49	9/66
4786	4/47	9/49	8/66	4856	12/44	5/49	2/67	4926	2/46	8/48	4/68
4787	5/47	11/48	11/65	4857	12/44	8/48	9/67	4927	2/46	1/50	9/67
4788	5/47	6/49	11/66	4858	12/44	6/49	12/67	4928	3/46	4/48	5/67
4789	5/47	1/50	12/64	4859	12/44	5/48	11/67	4929	3/46	4/48	6/68
4790	6/47	4/49	3/67	4860	12/44	10/49	1/67	4930	3/46	12/49	5/67

First No	Date into t'fic	Date BR No	With-drawn	First No	Date into t'fic	Date BR No	With-drawn	First No	Date into t'fic	Date BR No	With-drawn
4931	4/46	5/48	10/65	5001	3/35	3/49	3/68	5071	5/35	8/48	7/67
4932	9/45	4/49	8/68	5002	3/35	10/48	7/65	5072	6/35	6/49	9/67
4933	10/45	2/49	10/67	5003	3/35	10/48	5/67	5073	6/35	8/48	8/68
4934	10/45	2/50	9/67	5004	3/35	5/48	9/66	5074	6/35	6/48	9/65
4935	10/45	7/48	10/66	5005	3/35	9/48	1/68	5075	2/35	6/49	9/67
4936	11/45	11/49	8/67	5006	3/35	5/49	9/67	5076	3/35	4/48	6/68
4937	11/45	12/48	5/67	5007	3/35	12/48	7/64	5077	3/35	4/50	8/65
4938	11/45	8/48	10/67	5008	3/35	7/48	6/64	5078	3/35	4/49	10/65
4939	11/45	3/49	9/67	5009	3/35	5/48	11/65	5079	3/35	5/48	3/67
4940	11/45	1/50	3/68	5010	3/35	1/49	8/63	5080	3/35	5/48	9/67
4941	12/45	10/49	11/66	5011	4/35	1/49	12/65	5081	3/35	4/48	10/65
4942	12/45	3/49	6/68	5012	4/35	9/49	10/66	5082	3/35	3/49	7/66
4943	12/45	8/49	9/67	5013	4/35	4/48	4/68	5083	3/35	3/48	12/67
4944	1/46	10/49	9/67	5014	4/35	5/48	6/67	5084	3/35	7/48	11/66
4945	1/46	12/48	10/66	5015	4/35	9/48	9/67	5085	3/35	7/48	12/62
4946	1/46	12/48	5/67	5016	5/35	12/48	7/66	5086	3/35	6/48	12/62
4947	2/46	5/50	6/68	5017	5/35	10/48	8/68	5087	3/35	4/48	7/63
4948	2/46	6/48	9/67	5018	5/35	3/50	12/66	5088	3/35	3/49	9/64
4949	2/46	2/49	6/68	5019	5/35	5/48	5/67	5089	4/35	10/48	8/67
4950	3/46	1/49	8/68	5020	8/34	6/48	12/65	5090	4/35	6/48	12/65
4951	3/46	5/48	11/66	5021	8/34	3/49	9167	5091	4/35	6/48	9/66
4952	3/46	7/48	10/66	5022	8/34	7/48	9/63	5092	4/35	12/48	12/67
4953	3/46	10/48	12/66	5023	8/34	10/48	9/63	5093	4/35	1/49	11/65
4954	4/46	11/48	9/66	5024	8/34	1/49	5/67	5094	4/35	6/49	2/67
4955	4/46	10/48	8/65	5025	8/34	2/50	8/68	5095	4/35	7/48	8/68
4956	4/46	12/49	6/66	5026	9/34	5/48	10/65	5096	4/35	3/48	8/68
4957	5/46	11/49	6/64	5027	9/34	11/48	5/68	5097	4/35	12/48	6/66
4958	5/46	6/48	3/67	5028	9/34	5/49	3/67	5098	4/35	8/48	12/62
4959	5/46	4/48	7/65	5029	9/34	12/48	10/66	5099	4/35	2/50	9/63
4960	5/46	3/49	1/66	5030	9/34	12/49	12/62	5100	5/35	5/48	9/63
4961	6/46	2/50	6/64	5031	9/34	11/48	6/67	5101	5/35	3/50	3/68
4962	6/46	9/48	12/67	5032	9/34	8/49	2/64	5102	5/35	5/48	1/65
4963	6/46	3/49	7/68	5033	9/34	11/48	12/66	5103	5/35	2/49	10/64
4964	7/46	5/50	10/67	5034	9/34	4/48	2/68	5104	5/35	11/50	6/68
4965	8/46	5/48	3/68	5035	9/34	7/48	11/64	5105	5/35	6/49	10/66
4966	8/46	10/48	9/66	5036	9/34	1/49	12/62	5106	5/35	2/49	1/67
4967	4/46	2/49	6/64	5037	9/34	5/48	11/65	5107	5/35	10/49	9/67
4968	4/46	9/48	6/64	5038	9/34	12/48	2/68	5108	5/35	1/49	12/65
4969	4/46	2/50	12/63	5039	10/34	8/49	8/67	5109	5/35	5/48	3/67
4970	4/46	7/48	9/65	5040	10/34	11/48	7/67	5110	6/35	4/49	8/68
4971	4/46	6/48	8/68	5041	10/34	1/49	12/67	5111	6/35	11/48	10/67
4972	4/46	12/48	11/66	5042	10/34	3/49	7/67	5112	6/35	7/50	10/66
4973	5/46	4/48	9/65	5043	10/34	9/49	11/67	5113	6/35	5/48	6/65
4974	5/46	6/48	6/66	5044	10/34	6/48	11/66	5114	6/35	1/50	1/68
4975	5/46	4/49	9/65	5045	10/34	4/48	10/66	5115	6/35	5/48	11/66
4976	5/46	1/49	2/64	5046	10/34	4/49	6/68	5116	6/35	4/48	7/67
4977	6/46	2/49	11/66	5047	10/34	8/48	7/66	5117	6/35	10/48	10/65
4978	6/46	9/48	7/65	5048	10/34	1/50	11/67	5118	6/35	5/49	10/66
4979	6/46	9/48	7/65	5049	10/34	4/48	8/63	5119	6/35	4/48	12/62
4980	6/46	11/49	7/65	5050	11/34	9/49	8/67	5120	6/35	2/49	7/67
4981	7/46	1/49	1/67	5051	11/34	6/49	11/66	5121	6/35	8/48	6/64
4982	9/46	11/48	5/67	5052	11/34	5/48	9/67	5122	6/35	4/48	4/64
4983	9/46	6/48	9/67	5053	11/34	6/48	11/66	5123	7/35	4/48	9/63
4984	9/46	3/49	11/66	5054	11/34	6/48	2/68	5124	7/35	4/48	5/67
4985	10/46	6/48	11/67	5055	11/34	1/49	8/68	5125	5/35	7/48	12/62
4986	10/46	12/48	5/67	5056	11/34	10/48	8/67	5126	5/35	6/48	5/67
4987	11/46	6/48	10/66	5057	12/34	5/48	8/67	5127	5/35	3/49	11/66
4988	12/46	8/48	12/67	5058	12/34	6/49	10/66	5128	5/35	5/49	9/66
4989	12/46	7/48	2/67	5059	12/34	1/49	7/67	5129	5/35	2/49	9/66
4990	12/46	5/49	9/67	5060	12/34	8/48	3/67	5130	5/35	5/48	11/67
4991	12/46	5/48	5/67	5061	12/34	4/48	11/67	5131	5/35	10/49	4/68
4992	1/47	12/48	12/66	5062	12/34	6/49	4/67	5132	5/35	4/49	3/67
4993	1/47	12/48	12/67	5063	12/34	6/48	10/66	5133	5/35	9/48	2/68
4994	1/47	6149	7/64	5064	12/34	3/50	3/67	5134	5/35	9/48	8/68
4995	2/47	2/49	11/66	5065	12/34	9/48	4/68	5135	5/35	8/48	10/67
4996	2/47	3/49	4/64	5066	1/35	6/48	2/64	5136	5/35	1/49	10/64
4997	3/47	12/48	5/67	5067	1/35	11/48	10/67	5137	6/35	9/48	12/66
4998	3/47	6/48	4/67	5068	1/35	1/49	12/65	5138	6/35	11/48	9/66
4999	3/47	6/48	9/66	5069	1/35	4/48	6/67	5139	6/35	10/48	8/67
5000	2/35	1/49	10/67	5070	5/35	3/49	5/67	5140	6/35	1/49	9/66

First No	Date into t'fic	Date BR No	With-drawn	First No	Date into t'fic	Date BR No	With-drawn	First No	Date into t'fic	Date BR No	With-drawn
5141	6/35	9/48	3/67	5211	11/35	6/49	5/67	5281	11/36	7/49	12/67
5142	6/35	10/49	4/65	5212	11/35	10/48	8/68	5282	11/36	6/48	5/68
5143	6/35	8/49	12/65	5213	11/35	3/48	12/66	5283	11/36	6/48	1/67
5144	6/35	3/50	6/64	5214	11/35	9/48	12/66	5284	12/36	2/49	5/68
5145	6/35	3/49	11/67	5215	11/35	10/48	10/67	5285	12/36	9/48	12/67
5146	6/35	5/48	6/65	5216	11/35	9/48	2/66	5286	12/36	3/49	3/65
5147	6/35	1/49	5/67	5217	11/35	5/48	11/66	5287	12/36	8/49	8/68
5148	6/35	3/51	12/65	5218	11/35	6/48	4/66	5288	12/36	5/48	11/67
5149	6/35	1/49	6/68	5219	11/35	6/48	9/67	5289	12/36	9/48	11/66
5150	6/35	9/48	3/68	5220	11/35	4/49	9/66	5290	12/36	7/50	6/68
5151	6/35	8/48	12/62	5221	11/35	5/49	12/67	5291	12/36	8/48	10/65
5152	6/35	1/49	12/62	5222	12/35	2/49	2/67	5292	12/36	3/48	11/67
5153	6/35	5/48	6/64	5223	12/35	7/48	12/66	5293	12/36	1/49	8/65
5154+	6/35	1/49	11/66	5224	12/35	8/48	11/66	5294	12/36	4/49	3/68
5155+	7/35	9/48	11/64	5225	8/36	5/48	10/67	5295	12/36	5/49	12/67
5156+	7/35	9/48	8/68	5226	8/36	2/49	9/67	5296	12/36	12/50	2/68
5157+	7/35	5/48	12/62	5227	8/36	7/49	1/68	5297	12/36	3/49	9/67
5158+	7/35	6/48	7/64	5228	8/36	2/49	3/67	5298	12/36	4/49	9/67
5159	7/35	6/49	12/62	5229	8/36	5/48	9/65	5299	1/37	12/48	11/67
5160	7/35	8/48	9/66	5230	8/36	12/48	8/65	5300	1/37	6/49	12/65
5161	7/35	5/49	11/66	5231	8/36	6/48	8/68	5301	1/37	8/49	7/65
5162	8/35	7/48	11/66	5232	8/36	6/49	11/67	5302	1/37	8/48	7/67
5163	8/35	10/48	5/65	5233	8/36	3/49	5/66	5303	1/37	5/48	6/67
5164	8/35	8/48	8/66	5234	8/36	7/48	9/67	5304	1/37	5/49	8/67
5165	8/35	11/48	12/62	5235	8/36	9/49	1/66	5305	1/37	6/48	8/68
5166	8/35	4/48	9/63	5236	8/36	4/48	12/67	5306	1/37	5/48	1/65
5167	8/35	4/48	5/67	5237	8/36	12/49	9/65	5307	1/37	10/48	10/67
5168	8/35	3/48	9/66	5238	8/36	2/50	12/66	5308	1/37	5/48	8/67
5169	8/35	9/48	12/62	5239	8/36	2/49	9/67	5309	1/37	10/48	9/66
5170	8/35	5/48	3/64	5240	8/36	3/50	1/67	5310	1/37	5/50	8/68
5171	8/35	5/48	10/65	5241	9/36	12/48	9/67	5311	2/37	12/48	10/66
5172	8/35	12/48	6/64	5242	9/36	8/48	6/67	5312	2/37	5/48	6/68
5173	8/35	9/48	7/64	5243	9/36	8/49	9/67	5313	2/37	6/49	2/65
5174	8/35	2/49	12/62	5244	9/36	4/49	7/63	5314	2/37	12/48	11/65
5175	8/35	6/49	7/63	5245	9/36	5/48	8/65	5315	2/37	6/49	8/63
5176	8/35	6/49	8/66	5246	9/36	4/50	12/67	5316	2/37	9/48	3/68
5177	9/35	5/48	7/66	5247	9/36	3/49	4/67	5317	2/37	2/49	11/63
5178	9/35	12/48	1/65	5248	9/36	11/48	2/66	5318	2/37	9/48	8/68
5179	9/35	6/48	12/62	5249	9/36	4/48	12/66	5319	2/37	5/48	5/67
5180	9/35	4/49	9/65	5250	9/36	9/49	3/67	5320	2/37	11/48	10/63
5181	9/35	5/48	1/66	5251	9/36	3/48	12/63	5321	2/37	10/48	10/67
5182	9/35	10/48	3/66	5252	9/36	6/48	3/66	5322	2/37	6/49	9/66
5183	9/35	6/50	10/64	5253	9/36	5/48	3/68	5323	2/37	6/48	9/67
5184	9/35	7/48	9/65	5254	10/36	3/49	4/68	5324	2/37	10/49	8/67
5185	9/35	8/48	6/66	5255	10/36	5/49	6/68	5325	3/37	3/50	8/66
5186	9/35	9/48	9/67	5256	10/36	6/48	6/67	5326	3/37	4/48	3/67
5187	9/35	11/48	5/68	5257	10/36	6/49	11/65	5327	3/37	11/48	1/65
5188	9/35	7/49	7/67	5258	10/36	6/48	3/68	5328	3/37	9/48	9/67
5189	9/35	8/49	7/63	5259	10/36	6/48	12/67	5329	3/37	11/48	11/66
5190	10/35	12/48	5/68	5260	10/36	5/48	8/68	5330	3/37	3/49	8/68
5191	10/35	7/50	7/67	5261	10/36	4/48	10/67	5331	3/37	7/48	11/67
5192	10/35	6/48	8/65	5262	10/36	8/48	8/68	5332	3/37	11/48	11/66
5193	10/35	7/49	9/67	5263	10/36	8/48	10/67	5333	3/37	5/48	6/66
5194	10/35	3/48	4/65	5264	10/36	5/48	9/67	5334	3/37	9/48	6/65
5195	10/35	6/48	7/66	5265	10/36	1/49	5/62	5335	3/37	10/48	7/62
5196	10/35	10/48	12/67	5266	10/36	6/48	12/62	5336	3/37	5/48	1/67
5197	10/35	11/49	1/67	5267	10/36	11/48	10/67	5337	4/37	11/48	2/65
5198	10/35	12/49	9/67	5268	10/36	5/48	8/68	5338	4/37	5/48	10/66
5199	10/35	8/50	8/63	5269	11/36	4/49	8/68	5339	4/37	10/49	6/67
5200	10/35	2/49	7/68	5270	11/36	11/48	9/67	5340	4/37	12/48	4/67
5201	10/35	3/49	4/68	5271	11/36	9/48	9/67	5341	4/37	4/49	1/67
5202	10/35	12/48	6/68	5272	11/36	4/48	10/65	5342	4/37	1/50	8/68
5203	11/35	8/49	6/68	5273	11/36	6/49	9/67	5343	4/37	3/49	6/67
5204	11/35	8/49	1/67	5274	11/36	1/49	5/67	5344	4/37	11/48	8/66
5205	11/35	6/48	10/66	5275	11/36	10/48	10/67	5345	4/37	12/48	5/68
5206	11/35	8/49	8/68	5276	11/36	8/48	1/67	5346	4/37	4/49	6/67
5207	11/35	12/48	9/66	5277	11/36	8/48	2/67	5347	4/37	9/48	11/67
5208	11/35	11/48	10/67	5278	11/36	10/48	6/67	5348	4/37	5/49	8/66
5209	11/35	5/49	6/68	5279	11/36	8/48	3/68	5349	5/37	8/48	11/67
5210	11/35	11/48	4/66	5280	11/36	11/48	11/67	5350	5/37	8/49	8/68

First No	Date into t'fic	Date BR No	With- drawn	First No	Date into t'fic	Date BR No	With- drawn	First No	Date into t'fic	Date BR No	With- drawn
5351	5/37	11/48	8/65	5401	8/37	7/48	11/61	5451	12/37	11/48	11/66
5352	5/37	3/50	4/67	5402	8/37	4/48	4/67	5452	9/38	11/48	12/62
5353	5/37	2/49	7/68	5403	8/37	5/48	9/66	5453	9/38	3/49	12/62
5354	5/37	2/49	11/65	5404	8/37	12/48	5/67	5454	9/38	2/49	8/67
5355	5/37	9/48	12/62	5405	9/37	6/49	8/67	5455	9/38	8/48	8/67
5356	5/37	3/49	6/64	5406	9/37	6/49	7/67	5456	10/38	4/48	12/64
5357	5/37	4/48	12/66	5407	9/37	11/48	8/68	5457	10/38	8/48	9/63
5358	5/37	6/48	12/63	5408	9/37	5/49	11/66	5458	10/38	11/48	12/62
5359	5/37	7/48	5/67	5409	9/37	11/49	8/67	5459	10/38	5/48	5/64
5360	5/37	4/48	9/65	5410	9/37	6/48	9/66	5460	10/38	11/48	6/65
5361	5/37	8/48	2/64	5411	9/37	4/48	5/68	5461	10/38	9/48	8/66
5362	5/37	1/49	10/65	5412	9/37	9/49	8/67	5462	11/38	3/49	6/64
5363	6/37	7/48	10/67	5413	9/37	3/49	9/64	5463	11/38	10/48	11/66
5364	6/37	10/48	8/66	5414	10/37	8/49	2/65	5464	11/38	5/48	10/66
5365	6/37	3/48	12/66	5415	10/37	3/49	11/67	5465	11/38	5/49	2/64
5366	6/37	6/48	4/64	5416	10/37	6/49	7/65	5466	11/38	3/49	2/67
5367	6/37	4/48	11/63	5417	10/37	12/48	7/67	5467	11/38	6/48	12/66
5368	6/37	2/49	11/67	5418	10/37	8/48	2/66	5468	12/38	3/49	6/64
5369	6/37	12/50	3/67	5419	10/37	5/48	9/66	5469	12/38	4/48	11/66
5370	6/37	11/49	8/66	5420	10/37	6/50	6/68	5470	12/38	11/48	9/64
5371	6/37	12/48	4/67	5421	10/37	9/50	2/68	5471	12/38	4/48	7/65
5372	6/37	2/49	11/66	5422	10/37	6/48	9/66	5472	4/43	6/48	9/66
5373	6/37	9/48	9/67	5423	10/37	4/48	5/67	5473	5/43	10/49	11/66
5374	6/37	12/50	11/67	5424	10/37	12/48	4/68	5474	5/43	8/48	9/66
5375	6/37	2/49	1/68	5425	10/37	9/48	10/67	5475	6/43	6/48	9/66
5376	6/37	8/48	3/68	5426	10/37	8/50	3/68	5476	7/43	10/49	1/64
5377	6/37	5/48	12/67	5427	10/37	1/49	8/66	5477	7/43	9/48	8/66
5378	7/37	4/48	3/65	5428	10/37	9/48	9/67	5478	8/43	9/48	12/66
5379	7/37	5/49	7/65	5429	11/37	2/49	8/65	5479	8/43	3/49	6/64
5380	7/37	6/48	3/65	5430	11/37	7/48	9/66	5480	8/43	12/48	8/66
5381	7/37	6/49	5/68	5431	11/37	6/49	12/67	5481	9/43	11/48	9/67
5382	7/37	3/49	6/68	5432	11/37	8/49	10/66	5482	9/43	5/48	6/64
5383	7/37	1/49	2/67	5433	11/37	5/48	3/66	5483	9/43	9/48	12/66
5384	7/37	3/49	6/64	5434	11/37	9/48	8/66	5484	10/43	11/48	2/64
5385	7/37	5/48	11/66	5435	11/37	2/49	6/68	5485	10/43	10/48	10/63
5386	7/37	7/48	8/68	5436	11/37	6/48	4/68	5486	10/43	9/48	12/65
5387	7/37	1/49	3/65	5437	11/37	6/49	10/67	5487	11/43	5/48	6/64
5388	7/37	3/49	8/68	5438	11/37	9/48	8/66	5488	11/43	1/49	11/66
5389	7/37	4/48	10/65	5439	11/37	8/48	10/65	5489	11/43	10/48	11/66
5390	8/37	10/49	8/68	5440	11/37	8/48	9/67	5490	12/43	6/48	12/66
5391	8/37	5/49	2/68	5441	12/37	3/50	2/67	5491	12/43	5/48	7/65
5392	8/37	9/49	5/68	5442	12/37	4/48	8/66	5492	1/44	9/48	12/66
5393	8/37	4/49	9/66	5443	12/37	9/48	8/65	5493	1/44	1/50	1/68
5394	8/37	8/48	7/68	5444	12/37	12/48	8/68	5494	1/44	1/49	9/67
5395	8/37	6/48	3/68	5445	12/37	5/50	6/68	5495	2/44	5/49	3/67
5396	8/37	6/48	2/66	5446	12/37	9/49	2/67	5496	2/44	6/49	6/64
5397	8/37	5/48	8/68	5447	12/37	11/48	8/68	5497	4/44	6/49	6/64
5398	8/37	6/50	9/65	5448	12/37	6/48	8/67	5498	4/44	6/49	6/65
5399	8/37	10/50	12/66	5449	12/37	2/49	11/67	5499	4/44	8/48	8/65
5400	8/37	6/48	5/64	5450	12/37	8/49	11/67				

+ Named locomotives

5154 *Lanarkshire Yeomanry*	5156 *Ayrshire Yeomanry*	5158 *Glasgow Yeomanry*
5155 *Queens Edinburgh*	5157 *The Glasgow Highlander*	

* Non-standard fittings:—

Roller bearings 44668—97, 44748—67,
Caprotti valve gear 44686/7, 44738—57,
Stephenson link motion 44767,
Double chimney 44755—7/65—7 (No. 44767 altered to single chimney 1953),
Steel fireboxes 44718—27,
Electric headlights 44658, 44755—7/65—7 (removed in 1952)

CHAPTER FIVE

BRITISH RAILWAYS CLASS 5MT

Though the Black Five design of 1945-47 was the general base from which was built up the BR standard Class 5MT 4-6-0 of series 73000, and the LMSR 3B sloping-throatplate boiler was adopted except for details and fittings, the two locomotive types were different in linear dimensions, wheels, and cylinders, and were quite distinct in appearance. All the mechanical details followed BR's new concepts, though some of these were founded on Ivatt's practice through the last years of the LMSR. These included simplicity, visibility and accessibility of parts, good axlebox performance, simplified shed preparation and driver's inspection, mechanical lubrication of cylinders, valves and axleboxes, grease lubrication for valve motion, brake and suspension pins, reduction in shed disposal time, and efforts to reduce slipping to a minimum.

Endeavours to reduce preparation time were in a certain sense wasted, for by the agreements of that period the time allowed a driver was based on the heating surface of the locomotive, 1500sq ft being the dividing line. Thus less time was allowed for a Midland three-cylinder compound with three drive lines, six inside eccentrics and a number of inaccessible details than for a BR Class 5MT specifically designed throughout to economise in time. A postulate of the detail design of the 5MT was that the engine should be able to go two years between major shoppings, which in the event meant a maximum of 130,000 miles but more usually around 80,000.

From the beginning an axle load of 19¾ tons was accepted, along with a weight distribution of 3.75 tons/ft of coupled wheelbase, 2.45 tons/ft of engine-and-tender wheelbase, and 2.05 tons/ft of overall length, contrasted with 18, 3.55, 2.35 and 1.98 tons in early Black Fives. Locomotive working order weight was five per cent more than that of a standard Black Five, but only one per cent above that of a roller-bearing example. The reduced route availability was somewhat ameliorated in that many routes had been up-graded since 1934-35; later came further amelioration by the closing of many secondary lines.

Appearance was altered mainly by the cab shape and by the long high running plate with deep valance which had a sharp drop down at the front, to which two footsteps were bolted. A major difference was that the running plate, valance and cab were supported by the boiler and not by the main frame. In theory there would be no trouble from differential vibration or expansion, and numerous pipes and fittings were clipped to the running plate to obviate loosening. An exception to this arrangement was the front drop section forward of the cylinders, which was carried by the frames.

Construction of the locomotives began in 1951 and continued until 1957, though only one locomotive was completed in 1952. Derby built the first 100 engines under five BR (LMR) lot numbers; Doncaster and Derby shared the remaining seventy-two locomotives. Crewe, parent of the Black Fives and constructor of 241 of them and of the boilers for all the railway-built ones, built not a single BR Class 5MT, but manufactured all 130 boilers used in the engines built at Derby and all twelve spares

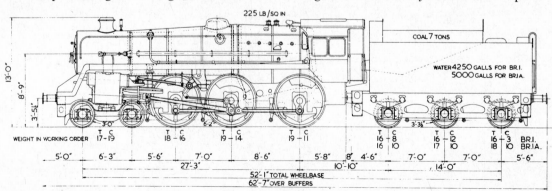

Left: **Fig 24** Diagram of BR Class 5MT standard 4-6-0 with Walschaerts motion and piston valves; type 1 tender.

Above: Left-hand side of brand-new standard piston-valve Class 5MT at Bath in 1954. BR model 1C tender attached. With this batch, Nos. 73050-59, began the plain rectangular-section coupling rods. Tri-tone chime whistle on smokebox. *(Ivo Peters)*

that were constructed. Darlington built thirty-two boilers for engines built at Doncaster, and Doncaster itself built the remaining ten.

Basic particulars of all Class 5MT deliveries are given in Table XVII, which shows, incidentally, the steep rise in construction costs compared with LMSR times. A chronic feature of pre-Grouping, Group and nationalised

British railways remained: inability to make any reasonably close estimate of construction cost. Actual prices of the 5MTs ranged from 18 to 34 per cent above the sanctioned amounts.

The first fifty engines were allocated to the LMR and ScR, but eventually all regions got allocations of new 5MTs. No names were given at first; but in 1959-61 the Southern Region

TABLE XVII BR STANDARD CLASS 5MT 4—6—0 DELIVERIES

Programme year	Running Nos	Year of Delivery	BR Lot No	Works	Works order	Cost per engine & tender	Tender BR Type/Nos	Region of first allocation
1951	73000—4	1951	222	Derby	O—5122	£17,603	1/794—8	LM
	73005—9	1951	222	Derby	O—5122	£17,603	1/799—803	Sc
	73010—29	1951—2	222	Derby	O—5122	£17,603	1/804—23	LM
1952	73030—9	1953	230	Derby	O—6280	£19,974	1/864—73	Sc
	73040—9	1953	230	Derby	O—6280	£19,974	1/874—83	LM
1953	73050—2	1954	235	Derby	O—6735	£20,682	1G/989—91	S
	73053/4	1954	235	Derby	O—6735	£21,171	1H/992/3	LM
	73055—9	1954	235	Derby	O—6735	£21,004	1H/994—8	Sc
	73060—4	1954	235	Derby	O—8035	£21,004	1H/999—1003	Sc
	73065—74	1954	235	Derby	O—8035	£21,171	1C/1004—13	LM
1954	73075—9	1955	241	Derby	N—8241	£21,909	1C/1201—5	Sc
	73080—9	1955	241	Derby	N—8241	£21,750	1B/1282—6	S
1955	73090—9	1955	245	Derby	N—8845	£22,490	1C/1272—81	LM
	73100—4	1955	1395	Doncaster	402	£21,460(2)	1B/1206—15	Sc
	73105—9	1955—6	1395	Doncaster	404	£21,560(2)	1B/1287—91	S
	73110—9	1955	1396	Doncaster	403	£21,183(2)	1F/1292—1301	S
	73120—4	1956	1395	Doncaster	404	£21,560(2)	1B/1302—6	Sc
1956	73125—34(1)	1956	247	Derby	N—9247	£28,075	1B/1413—22	W
	73135—44(1)	1956	247	Derby	N—9249	£28,075	1C/1423—32	LM
	73145—54(1)	1957	247	Derby	N—9250	£28,075	1B/1433—42	Sc
	73155—9	1956—7	1401	Doncaster	406	£25,606(2)	1B/1443—7	E
	73160—4	1957	1401	Doncaster	406	£25,606(2)	1B/1448—52	NE
	73165—71	1957	1401	Doncaster	407	£25,606(2)	1B/1453—9	NE

(1) Caprotti valve motion; (2) Excludes extra and capital charges included in remainder and averaging about £1,600 per locomotive.

Left: Front end of a standard model of the Class 5MT showing array of front footsteps and the brake and train-heating connections. *(Ivo Peters)*

Right: Boiler of Class 5MT, an almost exact copy of the 28-element superheater sloping-throatplate 3B boiler of the LMSR Black Fives. Gland and arm for regulator gear on barrel below dome; top feed on front ring; brackets for running plate along lower half of barrel.

Below right: BR Class 5MT of the first batch under erection at Derby in April 1951, showing cab and the rearward-extending footplate attached to the boiler.

named the twenty engines, Nos. 73080-89 and 73110-19 allocated to it in 1955, using names (but not the nameplates) of withdrawn King Arthur class 4-6-0s. These names are given in Table XVIII. The 1955 allocation was not the first SR experience with 5MTs, for three (Nos. 73003, 73015 and 73017) had been sent from the LMR to Nine Elms in June 1953 when the Merchant Navy Pacifics were temporarily out of service.

Boiler structure, tubeplates, tubes, flues, grate, heating surfaces and pressure were the same as in the 28-element superheater Black Fives, and the same flanging blocks were used. The boiler shell was of carbon-manganese steel in preference to the nickel-steel of the LMSR 3B

TABLE XVIII NAMES OF SOUTHERN REGION CLASS 5MT 4—6—0 LOCOMOTIVES

Loco No	Name	Date of naming
73080	Merlin	2/1961
73081	Excalibur	2/1961
73082	Camelot	8/1959
73083	Pendragon	10/1959
73084	Tintagel	11/1959
73085	Melisande	8/1959
73086	The Green Knight	12/1959
73087	Linette	5/1961
73088	Joyous Gard	5/1961
73089	Maid of Astolat	5/1959
73110	The Red Knight	1/1960
73111	King Uther	2/1961
73112	Morgan le Fay	4/1960
73113	Lyonesse	12/1959
73114	Etarre	3/1960
73115	King Pellinore	2/1960
73116	Iseult	9/1962
73117	Vivien	4/1961
73118	King Leodegrance	2/1960
73119	Elaine	6/1959

boiler, and the front end was supported on a fabricated steel saddle. The vertical grid-type regulator in the dome was operated by an outside pull rod and bell crank on the left-hand side, the firebox side stays were of Monel metal, the top-feed clacks were mounted separately at an angle of 30 degrees on each side of the front ring of the barrel and the normal single casing was omitted, and the steam manifold was now on the firebox top outside the cab.

Air space through the firebars at 32.6 per cent of the grate area was rather less than in the 3B boilers, but the major crew complaint on this score was rather that the air spaces between the bars were too narrow and blocked up quickly, so possibly full use of the rocking-grate fingers was not being made. All had self-cleaning smokeboxes with inclined plates and wire-mesh grids, fibreglass mattress lagging of barrel and firebox, self-emptying triple-hopper ashpans and eight-section rocking grates. Front and rear sections of the grate could be rocked separately, and both could be rocked for fire stirring or turned right round for dropping the fire.

At the back of the boiler the cab weatherboards were angled to obviate reflection through the front windows; the footplate was extended back over the tender to eliminate the hinged fall plate and to give a steadier firing floor.

Tractive effort at 85 per cent boiler pressure was 26,120 lb against the 25,455 lb of the Black Fives. As wheel diameter was increased to give standardisation with the Britannia Pacifics, and boiler pressure remained the same, cylinder bore was increased so that no reduction in tractive

effort compared with the Black Fives should ensue. On the other hand the slightly greater weight on the coupled wheels gave a rather higher factor of adhesion, which suited the BR design staff.

Piston-valve cylinders were unusual among those of BR standard types in being of cast-iron. All the others, including the Caprotti 5MTs, were of cast-steel with cast-iron bushes pressed in. Crossheads and slidebars were of the LNER 'overhung' type with triple bars, adopted as standard for six of the new BR classes, the LMSR 'alligator' form being given up for those types.

Walschaerts motion actuated 11in piston valves, and characteristics were: 1.69in lap, 0.25in lead, 7.7in maximum travel, 79 per cent maximum cut-off with a corresponding compression of 92 per cent. At 15 per cent cut-off the valve travel was 3.95in and the compression 62

per cent. Cylinder clearance was 11 per cent, and piston-swept volume was 10.4 per cent of the boiler steam space at half-glass; in the Black Fives it was 9.8 per cent. The plain blastpipe nozzle was 5¼in diameter set 11in below boiler centre line, but the orifice was soon reduced to 5⅛in. Thirty engines, Nos. 73125-54, built in 1956, were given Caprotti poppet valves and motion to an outside-drive layout based on that of the last two Black Fives; the official diagrams showed the same weights and distribution as the standard model, viz 76 tons full, 58 tons of adhesion weight, and 69.25 tons empty.

The locomotive wheelbase was within an inch of that of the early (1934-46) Black Fives, but the coupled wheelbase was 6in longer, and a new side-bearer bogie was devised that had a wheelbase 3in shorter, and this was standard with the bogie of the Britannia Pacifics. All 5MTs and tenders had roller-bearing axleboxes

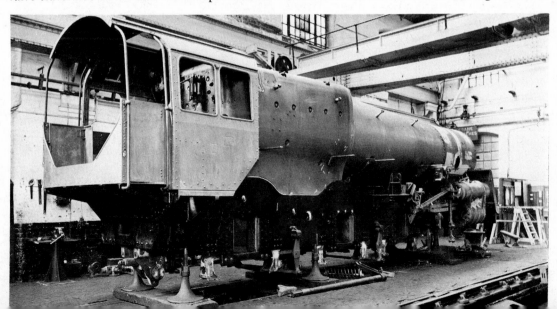

TABLE XIX GENERAL DIMENSIONS OF TWO BR CLASS 5MT VARIATIONS (1)

Locomotive numbers			73000–9	73125–54
Cylinders (2)		in	19 X 28	19 X 28
Wheel diam.		in	74	74
Boiler pressure		psi	225	225
Coupled wheelbase	ft	in	15—6	15—6
Engine wheelbase	ft	in	27—3	27—3
No & od of tubes		in	151@1 7/8	151@1 7/8
No & od of flues		in	28@5 1/8	28@5 1/8
Free gas area	sq	ft	4.55	4.55
Length between tubeplates	ft	in	13—2 7/8	13—2 7/8
Evap hs — tubes & flues	sq	ft	1479	1479
firebox	sq	ft	171	171
total	sq	ft	1650	1650
Grate area	sq	ft	28.65	28.65
Superheating surface	sq	ft	369(2)	358
Max axle load		tons	19.7	19.7
Adhesion weight		tons	58.05	58.05
Locomotive weight wo		tons	76.0	76.0
Locomotive weight empty		tons	69.25	69.25
Valves			Piston	Poppet
Valve motion			Walschaerts	Caprotti
Tender: BR type			1	1B
Water capacity		gall	4,250	4,725
coal capacity		tons	7	7
tare		tons	23.15	23.15
laden weight		tons	47.2	51.25
Locomotive & tender weight wo		tons	123.2	127.5
Locomotive & tender wheelbase	ft	in	52—1	52—1
Locomotive & tender over buffers	ft	in	62—7	62—7

(1) For boiler dimensions see 3B sloping throatplate type in Table III; (2) 1 3/8 od/10 SWG elements, replaced by 1 3/8 od/9 SWG elements as from 1954.

throughout and manganese-steel liners to coupled boxes and horns, along with the link-and-pin (or Horwich) horn cross-stays and other frame and suspension details from LMSR practice. Frame thickness was 1¼in. Tyre fastening was of the Bulleid form with two small lips and no ring, adopted by BR in preference to the Gibson retaining ring.

Steam brakes were used on engine and tender, and vacuum equipment was installed for the train brakes. Nos. 73030-31 completed in 1953 additionally had Westinghouse equipment for train brakes; this was for trials only, and was removed later. Single brake blocks were applied

to the coupled wheels in place of the twin blocks of all Black Fives built 1938-51. A return was made to the Gresham & Craven driver's brake valve in place of the LMSR type.

Contrasted with the more numerous Black Fives built over a much longer period, few variations from standard were found in the BR Class 5MT. Timken roller bearings were applied to all except Nos. 73090-99 which had the SKF parallel-roller type. Nos. 73105-09 and 73120-24 had the Poultney reversing gear in place of the normal BR hand-screw type with screw and nut acting directly on the reversing-shaft arm, and actuated through a tubular shaft from the cab

Above: A delightful combination of old and new: an ex-Somerset & Dorset 2-8-0 No. 53808, of design dating back to 1913, pilots BR 5MT No. 73047 of 1953 build on the 9.25am (SO) Bournemouth-Manchester train at Shepton Mallet, September 1962. *(Ivo Peters)*

Below left: Top view of Class 5MT of 1953 construction with BR standard type 1 tender. *(Ivo Peters)*

handwheel, which was located endwise. Continuous blowdown, a standard feature, was not applied to Nos. 73050-52 or to 73055-64. Tablet-catching apparatus was fitted when new to Nos. 73075-79 of the Scottish Region.

The thirty Caprotti engines had steam and exhaust pipe layouts different from standard; and in those locomotives, Nos. 73125-54, other modifications from normal (some of which had been introduced earlier) were made and kept for the succeeding seventeen engines, Nos. 73155-71 with piston valves. These included rectangular-section coupling rods in place of I-section (a modification originating with No. 73050 and

followed thereafter); the front cab windows were hinged instead of fixed; and a BR standard whistle was put horizontally on the firebox top in front of the cab in place of the cable-operated tri-tone type on the smokebox top just behind the chimney (which had shown a tendency to stick open), and wing plates (side doors) were fitted to the cab instead of to the tender.

The first ten of the Caprottis were the first of the 73000 series to be allocated when new to the WR, and were fitted at Swindon with that region's form of automatic train control. Nos. 73012-15/17-23/32-39 also were fitted at Swindon with the WR-type automatic train control on being transferred to that region's stock book in 1956; Nos. 73032-39 had been officially on loan to the WR from new, and the others had hardly worked on the LMR to which they had been formally allocated.

As soon as the first batch of ten had been delivered, Rugby plant tests were initiated, first with No. 73008, and then later with No. 73030.

TABLE XX PERFORMANCE OF BR CLASS 5MT 4-6-0 (1)

Year	Eastern Region Mileage	Avail-ability %	L.M. Region Mileage	Avail-ability %	N.E. Region Mileage	Avail-ability %	Scottish Region Mileage	Avail-ability %	Southern Region Mileage	Avail-ability %	Western Region Mileage	Avail-ability %
1952	–	–	42,006	76	–	–	72,365	79	–	–	41,706	81
1953	–	–	35,151	68	–	–	65,188	74	–	–	(3)	(3)
1954	–	–	41,358	81	–	–	67,875	76	–	–	32,015	74
1955	–	–	41,804	76	–	–	49,274	77	37,053	67	30,300	71
1956	30,478	55	40,385	77	–	–	49,136	80	42,086	72	25,310	72
1957	(3)	(3)	41,442	78	–	–	49,784	81	41,301	70	(3)	(3)
1958	37,904	68	30,821	70	39,032	81	47,327	77	40,987	73	30,757	69
1959	41,805	(2)	37,043	(2)	30,498	(2)	43,152	(2)	37,586	(2)	30,642	(2)
1960	36,423	(2)	35,951	(2)	36,126	(2)	39,100	(2)	35,850	(2)	30,710	(2)

(1) Mileage given is average/loco/year; (2) Availability recording discontinued; (3) Figures not available.

Above: Superstructure (tank, bunker, front plate and coal hole) of BR model 1 tender as attached to 5MTs Nos. 73000-49 when new.

Below: **Fig 25** Diagram of BR Class 5MT 4-6-0 with Caprotti motion and poppet valves; type 1C tender.

With grade 1A coal the maximum evaporation just reached 25,000lb/hr; but with grade 2B coal no more than 18,000lb/hr could be attained, and this was inferior to the LNER class B1 and GWR Hall class 4-6-0s with similar fuels. The blastpipe nozzle thereupon was reduced to 5in diameter with a resultant increase to 22,000lb/hr, and a further reduction to 4⅞in gave almost 24,000lb/hr. Evaporation improvement thus was obtained only at the expense of greatly increased back pressure and specific coal consumption. On the test plant a rail thermal efficiency of 8.8 per cent was attained over a narrow range between 30 and 40mph and 8000 to 10,000lb tractive effort. Some further trials were made on the plant with No. 73031 and were unique in that supplementary superheat was given by electrical means.

Few modifications were made to the class after the last engine had been completed, for by then the time of steam was beginning to run out, and the cost of any modifications had small chance of being recouped. From 1958 the BR aws apparatus was installed gradually, but not all engines got it before withdrawal. Colouring was the standard BR black, red lined, with numbers on the cab sides and the power-classification just above. Lining was put right round the tender side, at first with the BR emasculated lion symbol inside, and later with the rolling wheel emblem. All smokebox doors carried the self-cleaning *SC* plate near the bottom. The few repaints from 1963 were without lining; but earlier than that, in the period 1957-61, both Swindon and Eastleigh turned out several engines on repaint in the BR standard fully-lined passenger engine green, and then a few in unlined green.

Six BR tender types were attached to the 172 locomotives; all had the same intermediate coupling and connections and could be used indiscriminately without alteration. They were of more compact form than the Stanier type and had the shorter wheelbase of 14ft. Of the six models attached when new, as indicated in Table XVII, type 1 carried 4250 gallons of water and 7 tons of coal and weighed 49.15 tons all on; type 1B had 4725 gallons, 7 tons and 51.25 tons; type 1C had 4725 gallons, 9 tons, and 53.25 tons; type 1F had 5625 gallons, 7 tons and 55.5 tons, and had a tare of 23.15 tons; type 1G had 5000 gallons, 7 tons, and 52.5 tons; and type 1H had 4250 gallons, 7 tons, and 49.15 tons though it differed in some respects from type 1. Types 1F and 1G had no water pick-up.

All were of combined welded and riveted construction as regards superstructure, the tank, self-trimming bunker and front plate being welded up as one but with surge plates, tank stiffeners and bunker stiffeners riveted in. Types 1 and 1G had an inset coal bunker that

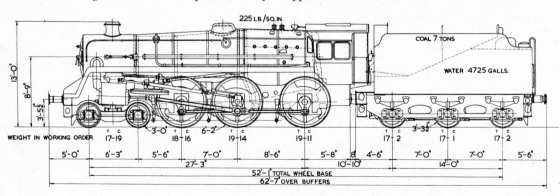

gave the crew a backward view on each side. Types 1B, 1C and 1F were not inset, and the high full-width sides had in-curved tops like a Stanier tender. One difference from the LMSR 4000-gallon tenders was the much smaller wheel diameter, 39½in against 51in; the diameter used was the same as that of the Black Five bogie wheels, but the 5MT bogie wheels were only 36in. At a later stage a few of the 5MTs exchanged their tenders for the larger 1D type with high curved-in tops; as built these tenders had a steam-operated coal pusher and weighed 63 tons with 9 tons of coal and 4725 gallons of water.

Class 5MT engines had short lives, the maxima being the seventeen years of Nos. 73000/10 and the shortest the eight years of Nos. 73161/64. Withdrawal years of all are given in Table XXI, and the rate of withdrawal was fifteen in 1964, forty-two in 1965, thirty-nine in 1966, fifty-three in 1967, and twenty-three in 1968.

Two engines, Nos. 73050 and 73129 are preserved, the former by the Peterborough Locomotive Society and the latter (a Caprotti) by Derby Borough Corporation. Since being acquired for preservation No. 73050 has been named *City of Peterborough*. At the moment of writing (August 1976) a small move is on foot to rescue the remains of one of the SR named engines, No. 73082 *Camelot*—still in the hands of breakers ten years after withdrawal.

TABLE XXI BRITISH RAILWAYS CLASS 5MT LOCOMOTIVES

No	Date into t'fic	With-drawn	No	Date into t'fic	With-drawn	No	Date into t'fic	With-drawn	No	Date into t'fic	With-drawn
73000	4/51	3/68	73043	10/53	7/67	73086+	8/55	10/66	73129*	8/56	11/67
73001	5/51	12/65	73044	11/53	3/65	73087+	8/55	10/66	73130*	9/56	1/67
73002	5/51	3/67	73045	11/53	8/67	73088+	9/55	10/66	73131*	9/56	1/68
73003	5/51	12/65	73046	11/53	9/64	73089+	9/55	9/66	73132*	9/56	3/68
73004	6/51	10/67	73047	12/53	12/64	73090	10/55	10/65	73133*	9/56	6/68
73005	6/51	6/66	73048	12/53	10/67	73091	10/55	5/65	73134*	9/56	6/68
73006	6/51	3/67	73049	12/53	3/65	73092	10/55	7/67	73135*	10/56	3/68
73007	7/51	3/66	73050	4/54	6/68	73093	11/55	7/67	73136*	10/56	3/68
73008	7/51	9/65	73051	5/54	8/65	73094	11/55	5/67	73137*	11/56	6/67
73009	7/51	7/66	73052	5/54	12/64	73095	11/55	8/66	73138*	11/56	4/68
73010	8/51	6/68	73053	6/54	3/68	73096	11/55	11/67	73139*	11/56	5/67
73011	8/51	11/67	73054	6/54	8/65	73097	12/55	5/67	73140*	11/56	10/67
73012	8/51	11/64	73055	6/54	5/66	73098	12/55	3/66	73141*	12/56	7/67
73013	8/51	5/66	73056	7/54	6/65	73099	12/55	10/66	73142*	12/56	4/68
73014	9/51	7/67	73057	7/54	3/66	73100	8/55	1/67	73143*	12/56	6/68
73015	9/51	8/65	73058	7/54	11/64	73101	8/55	8/66	73144*	12/56	8/67
73016	9/51	12/66	73059	8/54	5/67	73102	9/55	12/66	73145*	1/57	9/66
73017	9/51	10/64	73060	8/54	5/67	73103	9/55	10/65	73146*	2/57	5/67
73018	10/51	7/67	73061	9/54	12/64	73104	9/55	10/65	73147*	2/57	8/65
73019	10/51	1/67	73062	10/54	6/65	73105	12/55	9/66	73148*	3/57	9/65
73020	10/51	7/67	73063	10/54	6/66	73106	12/55	6/65	73149*	3/57	12/66
73021	10/51	8/65	73064	10/54	5/67	73107	12/55	9/66	73150*	4/57	12/66
73022	10/51	4/67	73065	10/54	7/67	73108	12/55	12/66	73151*	4/57	8/66
73023	11/51	8/65	73066	10/54	4/67	73109	1/56	10/64	73152*	5/57	12/65
73024	11/51	11/64	73067	10/54	3/68	73110+	10/55	1/67	73153*	5/57	12/66
73025	11/51	10/67	73068	10/54	12/65	73111+	10/55	9/65	73154*	6/57	12/66
73026	11/51	3/67	73069	11/54	8/68	73112+	10/55	6/65	73155	12/56	7/67
73027	12/51	2/64	73070	11/54	4/67	73113+	10/55	1/67	73156	12/56	11/67
73028	12/51	12/66	73071	11/54	9/67	73114+	11/55	6/66	73157	12/56	5/68
73029	1/52	7/67	73072	12/54	10/66	73115+	11/55	3/67	73158	12/56	10/67
73030	6/53	8/65	73073	12/54	11/67	73116+	11/55	11/64	73159	1/57	10/67
73031	7/53	9/65	73074	12/54	9/64	73117+	11/55	3/67	73160	1/57	11/67
73032	7/53	8/65	73075	4/55	12/65	73118+	12/55	7/67	73161	2/57	12/64
73033	8/53	1/68	73076	5/55	8/64	73119+	12/55	3/67	73162	2/57	5/65
73034	8/53	3/68	73077	5/55	1/65	73120	1/56	12/66	73163	2/57	11/65
73035	8/53	1/68	73078	5/55	7/66	73121	1/56	2/66	73164	3/57	12/64
73036	9/53	9/65	73079	6/55	5/67	73122	1/56	9/65	73165	3/57	9/65
73037	9/53	7/67	73080+	6/55	12/66	73123	2/56	5/65	73166	3/57	12/65
73038	9/53	10/65	73081+	6/55	7/66	73124	2/56	12/65	73167	4/57	8/65
73039	9/53	9/67	73082+	6/55	6/66	73125*	7/56	6/68	73168	4/57	12/65
73040	10/53	5/68	73083+	7/55	9/66	73126*	7/56	4/68	73169	4/57	10/66
73041	10/53	6/65	73084+	7/55	12/65	73127*	8/56	11/67	73170	5/57	6/66
73042	10/53	8/65	73085+	8/55	7/67	73128*	8/56	5/68	73171	5/57	10/66

+ Named locomotives (See Table XVIII)   * Fitted with Caprotti valve gear

APPENDIX

JUBILEE TENDERS

Tenders attached to the Jubilees when new varied considerably from the intended allocation, largely because of a decision to give the larger Royal Scots Stanier-type tenders in place of the smaller Midland-Fowler type with which they had been running for six or seven years, and to effect this by an exchange with tenders allocated to new Jubilees.

The tenders *ordered* for the Jubilees were: type (*a*) (see Jubilee tender description in Chapter 2) for Nos. 5552-56; type (*b*) for Nos. 5607-16; type (*c*) for Nos. 5617-64; and type (*d*) for Nos. 5557-5606 and 5665-5742. The actual tenders first attached to the Jubilees are listed in Table A. Tender exchanges made with Royal Scots before the affected Jubilees entered service are shown in Table B; and the subsequent further changes with Royal Scot tenders, around

1936, after the Jubilees affected had been some time in service, are recorded in Table C.

Tenders attached originally to Nos. 5552-56 were actually *ordered* for five 2-8-0 locomotives that were to bear Nos. 13811-15, but these did not materialise and eventually were replaced by Stanier Class 8F Consolidations in 1935. Two extra 3500-gallon tenders of type (*c*) were intended for the first two Stanier 8F engines Nos. 8000-01, but were fitted in exchange to Jubilees Nos. 5665-66; the next tender went to No. 6170, and this displaced the allocated Stanier tenders on by three until No. 5671 was reached; then the next tender built for that batch went direct to Royal Scot No. 6127, so displacing the rest of the tenders by two until 5692 was reached. Nos. 5693-94 took the tenders intended for Nos. 5695-96, and so only Nos.

APPENDIX TABLE A ORIGINAL TENDER Nos JUBILEE CLASS 4—6—0

Loco Nos	Tender type	Tender Nos (actual)	Remarks
5552—6	Old standard 3,500g	4469—73	Intended for 2—8—0 Nos 13811—5 (Lot 92) never built.
5557—5606	Stanier 4,000g	9004—53	Built by NBL.
5607—16	Modified 3,500g	4564—73	
5617—64	New 3,500g	4600—18/24—9, 4619—23/ 30—47	Attached in order shown.
5665/6	New 3,500g	4648/9	Built for 2—8—0 Nos 8000/1 (Lot 115); allocated tenders (Nos 9134/5) attached to 2—8—0 Nos 8000/1.
5667—71	Stanier 4,000g	9137—41	Allocated tenders were Nos 9136—40 but No 9136 went to 4—6—0 No 6170.
5672—92	Stanier 4,000g	9143—63	Allocated tenders were Nos 9141—61 but No 9141 went to Jubilee No 5671, No 9142 was spare until attached to 4—6—0 No 6127. Nos 9153/61 were the first railway built welded tenders (to locomotives Nos 5682/90).
5693/4	Stanier 4,000g	9329/30	Allocated tenders were Nos 9162/3 which went to locomotives Nos 5691/2.
5695—5725	Old standard 3,500g	(see Table B)	Allocated tenders were Nos 9329—59, used as follows:— Nos 9329/30 to locos Nos 5693/4, Nos 9331—43 to Royal Scot 4—6—0, Nos 9344/5 to 4—6—2 Nos 6208/11*, Nos 9346—52 to Royal Scot 4—6—0, Nos 9353/4 to 4—6—2 Nos 6205/12*, Nos 9355—8 to Royal Scot 4—6—0, No 9359 to 4—6—2 No 6206*. *10 tons coal bunker and No 9359 fitted with coal pusher.
5726/7	Stanier 4,000g	9130, 9127	Transferred from 4—6—2 Nos 6209/06; allocated tenders Nos 9360/1 attached to 4—6—2 Nos 6210/09 (with 10 tons bunkers)
5728—37	Stanier 4,000g	9362—71	Attached as allocated.
5738/9	Stanier 4,000g	9066, 9065	Transferred from 4—6—2 Nos 6201/00; allocated tenders Nos 9372/3 attached to 4—6—2 Nos 6200/1 (with 10 tons bunkers).
5740	Old standard 3,500g	(see Table B)	Allocated tender No 9374 attached to 4—6—2 Nos 6203 (with 10 tons bunker).
5741/2	Stanier 4,000g	9125/8	Transferred from 4—6—2 Nos 6204/8; allocated tenders Nos 9375/6 attached to 4—6—2 Nos 6204/7 (with 10 tons bunkers).

5728-37 out of the last batch of forty-eight Jubilees (LMSR lot number 129) got new tenders—their correct ones. The balance was attached to twenty-four Royal Scots and twelve Princess Royal Pacifics, and those tenders were completed with a coal space of ten tons.

This complicated initial allocation was soon disturbed when a further thirty-nine type (a) old-standard tenders then running with Royal Scots were exchanged in 1936 with Stanier 4000-gallon tenders attached to Jubilees Nos. 5557, 5560-74, 5585-99, 5600-06, and 5679. Further, when in April 1935 the original No. 5552 exchanged numbers with the original 5642,

a three-way tender exchange was involved; the old number 5552 retained its original type (a) tender, but the new No. 5552 exchanged its type (c) 3500-gallon tender for the Stanier tender of No. 5559.

An opportunity to replace many of the type (a) old-standard tenders running with Jubilees arose when forty-five Class 4F 0-6-0s were built at Crewe and Derby between 1937 and 1941. When that locomotive order was placed the tenders were arranged to be of Stanier 4000-gallon type, but instead of being attached to the 0-6-0s a transfer was made so that Jubilees Nos. 5557, 5560-67, 5569, 5570, 5572-73, 5585,

APPENDIX TABLE B PRINCIPAL TENDER CHANGES, JUBILEES/ROYAL SCOTS (1)

Jubilee Loco No	Tender No	Ex-Royal Scot No	Jubilee Loco No	Tender No	Ex-Royal Scot No
5695	3923	6399	5711	3937	6116
5696	3921	6139	5712	3898	6144
5697	4243	6158(2)	5713	4244	6165
5698	4251	6166(2)	5714	3911	6124
5699	3917	6118	5715	3944	6119
5700	3913	6132	5716	4243	6168
5701	3945	6109	5717	3933	6121
5702	3940	6136	5718	3908	6125
5703	3935	6102	5719	4238	6151
5704	4246	6161(2)	5720	3901	6122
5705	4240	6155(2)	5721	3902	6100
5706	4226	6153	5722	3938	6133
5707	3936	6140(2)	5723	3905	6114
5708	4248	6163(2)	5724	4247	6162(2)
5709	3931	6152	5725	4242	6157(2)
5710	3909	6106	5740	3926	6130(2)

(1) All tender changes in this table were made before the Jubilee class engines entered traffic; all tenders were old standard 3,500g (2) Original tender of Royal Scot numbered.

APPENDIX TABLE C PRINCIPAL TENDER CHANGES, JUBILEES/ROYAL SCOTS (1)

Jubilee Loco No	Tender No	Ex-Royal Scot No	Jubilee Loco No	Tender No	Ex-Royal Scot No
5557	3918	6131	5589	3899	6107
5560	2863(3)	6127	5590	3896	6110
5561	3912	6149	5591	3920	6126
5562	3903	6143	5592	4245	6160(2)
5563	3897	6111	5593	3930	6123
5564	3914	6138	5594	3928	6134
5565	3900	6105	5595	3922	6137
5566	3932	6169	5596	3925	6129(2)
5567	3924	6128(2)	5597	3929	6142
5568	3907	6145	5598	3934	6141
5569	3916	6147	5599	4250	6159
5570	4249	6164(2)	5600	3941	6117
5571	3943	6146	5601	3906	6108
5572	4239	6154(2)	5602	4254	6135
5573	3919	6101	5603	4252	6167(2)
5574	3939	6115	5604	4235	6150(2)
5585	3915	6104	5605	3904	6113
5586	3942	6148	5606	4241	6156(2)
5587	4237	6112	5679	3927	6103
5588	3910	6120			

(1) All tender changes in this table were made after the Jubilee class engines had entered traffic; all tenders were old standard 3,500g; (2) Original tender of Royal Scot numbered; (3) Originally attached to 4P 4—4—0 Compound No 1058, then 4—6—0 super-pressure locomotive No 6399 *Fury* before going to Royal Scot No 6127.

APPENDIX TABLE D NEW 4,000 Gall TENDERS IN PLACE OF OLD STANDARD 3,500 Gall TYPE IN 1939—40

Loco No	Tender No	Loco No	Tender No	Loco No	Tender No
5556	9757	5587	9765	5607	9763
5557	9761	5588	9695	5608	9775
5560	9777	5590	9692	5609	9772
5561	9762	5591	9753	5610	9770
5562	9774	5592	9693	5611	9754
5563	9756	5593	9689	5614	9780
5564	9697	5594	9764	5615	9778
5565	9768	5596	9779	5698	9773
5566	9766	5598	9767	5699	9776
5567	9688	5599	9699	5721	9755
5569	9694	5600	9702	5722	9759
5570	9700	5601	9701	5723	9758
5572	9691	5602	9690	5724	9771
5573	9769	5604	9696	5726	9782
5585	9781	5606	9698	5740	9760

APPENDIX TABLE E 3,500 Gall TENDERS FITTED TO JUBILEES WHEN 4,000 Gall TENDERS WERE TAKEN FOR REBUILT PATRIOTS 1946—9

Loco No	Tender No	Ex-Patriot No	Loco No	Tender No	Ex-Patriot No
5556	4503(1)	5525	5600	4494(1)	5530
5557	4486(1)	5514	5611	4502(1)	5526
5561	4492	5522	5698	4472(1)	5545
5563	4496(1)	5531	5721	4501	5523
5585	4498(1)	5536	5722	4484(1)	5512
5587	45C7(1)	5534	5723	4512(1)	5540
5591	4504(1)	5527	5724	4508(1)	5535
5596	4485	5521	5726	4505(1)	5528
5598	4495(1)	5529	5740	4497(1)	5532

(1) Original tender of Patriot numbered.

APPENDIX TABLE F 4,000 Gall TENDERS BOUGHT FROM WD 1948

Jubilee Loco No	LMR Tender No	Ex—WD No
45554	10226	(1)
45585	10307	331
45611	10215	446
45725	10306	337

(1) No identity marks left on when tender returned.

5587-88, 5590-94, 5596, 5598-99, 5600-02, 5604, 5606 and 5726 again had Stanier tenders. Nos. 5607-11 and 5614-15 lost their type (b) tenders and got type (c) units. Nos. 5556, 5698-99, 5721-24 and 5740 got big Stanier tenders for the first time; the actual tender numbers are shown in Table D. For some reason No. 5590 was photographed officially attached to an old Midland Railway tender with coal rails but without upper side wings, but is not known to have run in this form.

Tender exchanges continued, and No. 5609 soon afterwards re-acquired a type (a) old-standard model; Nos. 5703 and 5726 made a direct swap of a type (a) Fowler and a type (d)

Stanier, and Nos. 5612-13 and 5616 lost their type (b) tenders and got type (a) units instead, so that by the mid-war period forty-two Jubilees were running with type (a) old-standard Fowler tenders. By this time Nos. 5558 and 5684 had been given type (c) tenders and Nos. 5643, 5645 and 5662 had Stanier tenders. The tender from No. 5643 went to Royal Scot No. 6104, which was thus unique in its class until 1961, when No. 46162 also got one, though not until No. 6104 (by then 46104) had lost its example.

The next large-scale tender exchange took place when the eighteen rebuilt Patriots of 1946-49 were given 4000-gallon Stanier tenders and their type (a) old-standard Fowlers were given in lieu of the Staniers to Jubilees Nos. 5556-57, 5561, 5563, 5585, 5587, 5591, 5596, 5598, 5609, 5611, 5698, 5721-24, 5726 and 5740, as shown in Table E.

For years frequent operating-department requests for more 4000-gallon tenders for the Jubilees had been made, largely because of the lack of self-trimming facilities and small coal content of the 3500-gallon type; and when well after the war four ex-WD Staniers became

APPENDIX TABLE G 4,000 Gall TENDERS TAKEN FROM 8F 2–8–0 IN EXCHANGE FOR 3,500 Gall TYPES 1958–64

Jubilee No	Tender No	Jubilee No	Tender No	Jubilee No	Tender No
45553	10301	45596	10750	45702	10248
45555	10365	45597	10736	45705	10758
45556	10216	45598	10752	45706	10747
45557	10329	45603	9671	45708	10294
45561	10387	45605	10381	45709	10366
45563	10418	45609	Not done	45710	10328
45568	10741	45612	10354	45712	10777
45571	10575	45613	10383	45717	?
45574	10367	45615	10152	45719	10327
45586	10742	45642	10232	45721	10067
45587	10095	45695	10780	45722	10787
45589	10288	45698	10206	45723	10330
45591	10545(1)	45700	10168	45726	10204
45595	9892	45701	10332	45740	9065(2)

(1) Ex-Class 5 4–6–0 No 44920; (2) Ex-Jubilee No 45739

available in the Middle East they were purchased, repaired, and attached in 1949 to Nos. 45554, 45585, 45611 and 45725 (see Table F).

Not until 1959 was the last substantial change made in tenders to eliminate the Fowler old-standard type (*a*) still attached to forty-two of the Jubilees on the LMR. The exchange was made with nominated Class 8F 2-8-0s, the tender numbers being as given in Table G. All but one of the planned exchanges was made, the exception being No. 45609 which was withdrawn in 1960 before an exchange could be made. Other Jubilees were still running on the ScR and ER/NER with Fowler 3500-gallon tenders, and of these Nos. 45697 and 45704 got 4000-gallon tenders by 1964. Meantime 3500-gallon type (*b*) tenders had reappeared on Nos. 45568 (1957-60), 45710 (1957-59), and 45719 (1957-58), and type (*c*) 3500-gallon tenders were given to Jubilees other than those already mentioned, *viz* Nos. 45557, 45575, 45584, 45593, 45602, 45607, 45615 and 45729-31.

Despite the numerous complicated changes enumerated in this appendix a surprising number of Jubilees retained the original *type* of tender, and thirty-three of these never changed tenders at all.

ACKNOWLEDGEMENTS

For much help in many directions the warm thanks of the authors are given to Messrs Brian Radford, B. J. Harding, T. J. Edgington, E. S. Cox, Murdoch Nicolson, A. G. Dunbar and D. H. Stuart; also to Mr G. S. W. Calder, chief mechanical and electrical engineer of British Railways, for his agreement to the first of the authors participating in this book.

INDEX